World Dynamics

JAY W. FORRESTER

WRIGHT-ALLEN PRESS, INC.
238 Main Street
Cambridge, Massachusetts 02142

Library of Congress catalog card number: 70-157752

To
Gordon S. Brown

Preface

Over the last several decades interest in economic development, population growth, and the world environment has expanded rapidly. As world-wide stresses have increased, many individuals and organizations have begun to study and to influence the changing aspects of the world situation. But it seems fair to observe that most of the activity has been addressed to separate facets of the world system. Little has yet been done to show how the many actions and forces are affecting one another to produce the total consequences that we observe. Now however, many persons are coming to believe that the interactions within the whole are more important than the sum of the separate parts. This book was undertaken as one step toward showing how the behavior of the world system results from mutual interplay between its demographic, industrial, and agricultural subsystems.

The present investigation grew from a 15-year program of exploring the dynamic structures of social systems and from a sequence of events in the summer of 1970 that focused the earlier background on the rapidly growing stresses within our largest social system—the world community. Beginning in 1957 with support of a grant from the Ford Foundation, the methods of "industrial dynamics" were developed as a way to understand and to design corporate policy. From that work has developed a general viewpoint about the feedback-loop structure of systems and their subsequent dynamic behavior. The resulting principles and practices have been finding ever broadening applications.

In 1968 along with John F. Collins and others, I extended the approach to the growth and stagnation characteristics of urban areas as described in my book *Urban Dynamics.* A timely grant from the Independence Foundation in Philadelphia supported formation of a group of staff and graduate students to penetrate more deeply into urban behavior. The existence of that group gave us the capability to respond to the events in the summer of 1970 that led to the present book and the continuing project on global dynamics.

On June 29, 1970, I attended a meeting of The Club of Rome in Bern, Switzerland. The Club of Rome is a private group numbering some 75 members from many countries who have joined together to find ways to understand better the changes now occurring in the world. The members act as private citizens. They are not in governmental decision-making positions. Their orientation is activist—that is, they wish to do more than study and understand. They wish to clarify the course of human events in a way that can be transmitted to governments and peoples to influence the trends of rising population, increasing pollution, greater crowding, and growing social strife.

At the time of the Bern meeting, The Club of Rome had already planned a project on "The Predicament of Mankind." Preliminary goals, a survey of methodologies, and a statement of the "problematique" had been prepared by Aurelio Peccei, Eduard Pestel, Alexander King, Hasan Ozbekhan, Hugo Thiemann, and others. The objective of the project is to understand the options available to mankind as societies enter the transition from growth to equilibrium. Man throughout history has focused on growth—growth in population, standard of living, and geographical boundaries. But in the fixed space of the world, growth must in time give way to equilibrium. Little is known about the social and economic forces that will accompany the entry into world equilibrium.

The June meeting was held to review the status of the project, which was about to begin. Discussion in the meeting revealed that a suitable methodology had not yet been identified to deal with the broad sweep of human affairs and the ways in which major elements of the world ecology interact with each other. Because the "system dynamics" approach as already developed at the Massachusetts Institute of Technology seemed well suited, the group was invited to Cambridge to determine firsthand if they agreed that the methods then existing would be suitable for the next step in the project. As a result, a meeting convened on July 20 for ten days of study, presentations, and discussion.

The dynamic model of world interactions described in this book was devised in the early part of July to form a basis for discussion at the conference. It must be considered a preliminary effort. But all models will be tentative, for new insights will continue to appear. Because a truly final model of the world system is unlikely ever to be achieved, and because of the widespread interest that has already been expressed in this effort, it seems appropriate to present the existing assumptions and implications in this book.

As a result of the July meeting, the Executive Committee of The Club of Rome decided to establish a one-year research program at M.I.T. An international team under the leadership of Professor Dennis L. Meadows is going beyond the model described here to explore more deeply the underlying assumptions and the several major subsystems that form the sectors of the total world system. Substantial extensions are being made into the dynamics of population, pollution, capital investment, and agriculture. The emerging results promise to extend greatly the understanding of world behavior. As of this writing, the new insights do not alter in any substantial way the broad implications reported here.

The continuing project, as well as the July conference, has been made possible by financial support to The Club of Rome from the Volkswagen Foundation (Stiftung Volkswagenwerk) in Germany.

Only broad aspects of the world system are discussed here, not the difficulties of implementing the changes that will be necessary if the present course of human events is to be altered. Many important variables are omitted. Aggregation is at such a high level that the distinctions between developed and underdeveloped countries do not appear explicitly. Most of the concepts in the world model reflect the attitudes and motivations of the recent past and present. Therefore the book does not incorporate the possible changes in human aspirations and values that might come from widespread recognition of the predicament facing mankind. All these and others are issues for future investigation. I hope this book contributes to the sense of urgency and also that it points to an effective direction for work by others who may choose to explore the alternatives for the future.

In spite of the tentative nature of the world model described here, various conclusions are drawn from it. Man acts at all times on the models he has available. Mental images are models. We are now using those mental models as a basis for action. Anyone who proposes a policy, law, or course of action is doing so on the basis of the model in which he, at that time, has the greatest confidence. Having defined with care the model contained herein, and having examined its dynamic behavior and implications, I have greater confidence in this world system model than in others that I now have available. Therefore, this is the model I should use for recommending actions. Those others who find this model more persuasive than the one they are now using presumably will wish to employ it until a better model becomes available.

It is to be hoped that those who believe they already have some different model that is more valid will present it in the same explicit detail, so that its assumptions and consequences can be examined and compared. To reject this model because of its shortcomings without offering concrete and tangible alternatives would be equivalent to asking that time be stopped. But the world will continue to turn. We always use the most acceptable model at any point in time. But how should we proceed so that the most acceptable model is also the best one that is available? We should try for three things. First, the best *existing* model should be identified at each point in time. Second, the best currently existing model should be used in preference to traditional models that may be less clear and less correct. Third, aggressive effort should be devoted to a continual improvement in the available models of the world system.

It seems traditional for explicit models of social systems to be greeted by vague criticisms about their lack of perfection. Instead, we need equally explicit alternatives with a demonstration that the alternative leads to a *different* and *more plausible* set of conclusions. By proposal and counter proposition our understanding of social systems can advance.

I am especially indebted to Gordon S. Brown, John F. Collins, Aurelio Peccei, and Eduard Pestel for encouragement and assistance in the many stages leading to this book. I also appreciate the helpful criticism of the manuscript from Richard Brown, Robert G. Erwin, John Henize, Dennis L. Meadows, John A. Seeger, and Carroll L. Wilson. Neither they nor The Club of Rome should be held responsible for the assumptions and interpretations presented here.

JAY W. FORRESTER

Massachusetts Institute of Technology
Cambridge, Massachusetts.
March, 1971.

Contents

1 Introduction

1.1 A World System

The world system is encountering new pressures. By "world system" we mean man, his social systems, his technology, and the natural environment. These interact to produce growth, change, and stress. It is not new to have great forces generated from within the socio-technical-natural system. But only recently has mankind become aware of rising forces that cannot be resolved by the historical solutions of migration, expansion, economic growth, and technology.*

The manifestations of stress in the world system are excessive population, rising pollution, and disparity in standards of living. But are growing population, pollution, and economic inequality causes or symptoms? Can they be ameliorated directly, or do the causes of stress lie elsewhere in the world system?

There is a growing awareness that past efforts to relieve stress in our social systems have often been, in retrospect, only efforts to suppress symptoms without altering the underlying causes. More and more, the world system is becoming tightly interrelated. An action in one sector of the system can produce consequences in another sector. Often the consequences are unintended and undesirable. We need to understand the ways in which the major factors are influencing one another on a world-wide scale if we are to have confidence that our actions will lead to improvement rather than to making matters worse.

Our knowledge and assumptions about the components of a system, even systems as complex as our social systems, can now be interrelated and examined through methods that have been developed in the last several decades. Such is done by organizing the individual concepts into a "model" that reveals the consequences and internal inconsistencies of our assumptions and fragments of knowledge. From such an examination can come a much improved understanding of the world system within which we are enmeshed.

This book sets forth a dynamic model of world scope, a model which interrelates population, capital investment, geographical space, natural resources, pollution, and food production. From these major sectors and their interactions

*See Peccei, References 8, 9, and 10.

appear to come the dynamics of change in the world system. Rising population creates pressures to increase industrialization, grow more food, and occupy more land. But more food, material goods, and land tend to encourage and permit larger populations. The growth in population, with its attendant industrialization and pollution, comes from circular processes in which each sector both enhances and feeds on other sectors. But in time, growth encounters limits set by nature. Land and natural resources become exhausted, and the pollution-dissipation capacity of the earth becomes overloaded.

The battle between the forces of growth and the restraints of nature may be resolved in a number of ways. Man, if he understands well enough and acts wisely, can choose a path out of the conflict of world pressures that is more favorable than present actions, attitudes, and policies portend. Such a path must be toward a non-growing and balanced condition of the world system. The challenge is to choose the best available transition from the past dynamics of growth to a future condition of world equilibrium.

Ever since Malthus stated his propositions relating population and food some 150 years ago, the validity of his assumption that food imposes an ultimate limit on population has been debated. The continued growth of population and the rise in the productivity of agriculture are often cited to refute Malthus. But it is undeniable that Malthus stated one ultimate barrier to unending population expansion. His assertion is not erroneous; it is merely incomplete.

Food supply may not be the first barrier to restrain rising population. Other forces within the world's socio-technological system may suppress further increase in population before starvation does.

Population, capital investment, pollution, food consumption, and standard of living have been growing exponentially throughout recorded history. Man has come to expect growth, to see it as the natural condition of human behavior, and to equate growth with "progress." We speak of the annual percentage growth in gross national product (GNP) and in population. Quantities that grow by a fixed percentage per year are exhibiting "exponential" growth. But exponential growth cannot continue indefinitely.

Pure exponential growth possesses the characteristic of behaving according to a "doubling time." Each fixed time interval shows a doubling of the relevant system variable. Exponential growth is treacherous and misleading. A system variable can continue through many doubling intervals without seeming to reach significant size. But then, in one or two more doubling periods, still following the same law of exponential growth, it suddenly seems to become overwhelming.

The psychological impact of exponential growth is seldom appreciated. Suppose that some ultimate physical limit stands in the way of a quantity that is growing exponentially. In all previous time before the limit is approached, the quantity is much smaller than the limit. The very existence of the limit may be unrealized. No clash between the growing quantity and the limit forces attention to the eventual pressures that must arise. Then suddenly, within one doubling interval, the quantity grows from half the limit to the limit. The stresses from overexpansion become highly visible; they can no longer be ignored. If the pressures created by approach to the limit are not great enough to suppress growth, then growth continues until the limit has been overstepped far enough to generate forces sufficient to inhibit growth.

Exponential growth is only significant in comparison to some relevant limit. The power and nature of exponential growth are best appreciated through an example. Suppose, for purposes of illustration, that we start with a population of 1 million people and that the number doubles every 50 years. Figure 1-1 is a tabulation of population for the subsequent 700 years. In 700 years the population rises from 1 million to 16,384 million.

The values of Figure 1-1 have been plotted as the solid line on the graph of Figure 1-2. A "crisis level" at 8,000 million people has been arbitrarily chosen as the point beyond which the pressures from conflict between growth and some limit become severe. In drawing a chart as in Figure 1-2, we tend to pick the vertical scale so that the point of concern lies about halfway up the page. It is this choice of scales which makes growth appear so steep and sudden, and not any change in the "law of growth" that has been governing the system. To illustrate that exponential growth seems to surge up toward any ultimate limit regardless of its value, suppose that the "crisis level" in Figure 1-2 were at 800 million people instead of 8,000 million. A second vertical scale, chosen so that the "crisis level" comes at 800, is shown inside the figure. The dashed line is drawn through points that are again taken from the values in Figure 1-1 but, for the dashed line, are plotted to the inner vertical scale. A reduction of the "crisis level" by a factor of 10 has caused growth to impinge on that lower limit some 170 years sooner than for the solid curve. Otherwise the sudden rise and shape of the clash between growth and the limit are the same.

The surprise that we experience from exponential change comes, not from any sudden alteration in the pattern of growth, but instead from the pressures of

Years	Millions of people
0	1
50	2
100	4
150	8
200	16
250	32
300	64
350	128
400	256
450	512
500	1,024
550	2,048
600	4,096
650	8,192
700	16,384

Figure 1-1 Population growth during 700 years, with a doubling time of 50 years.

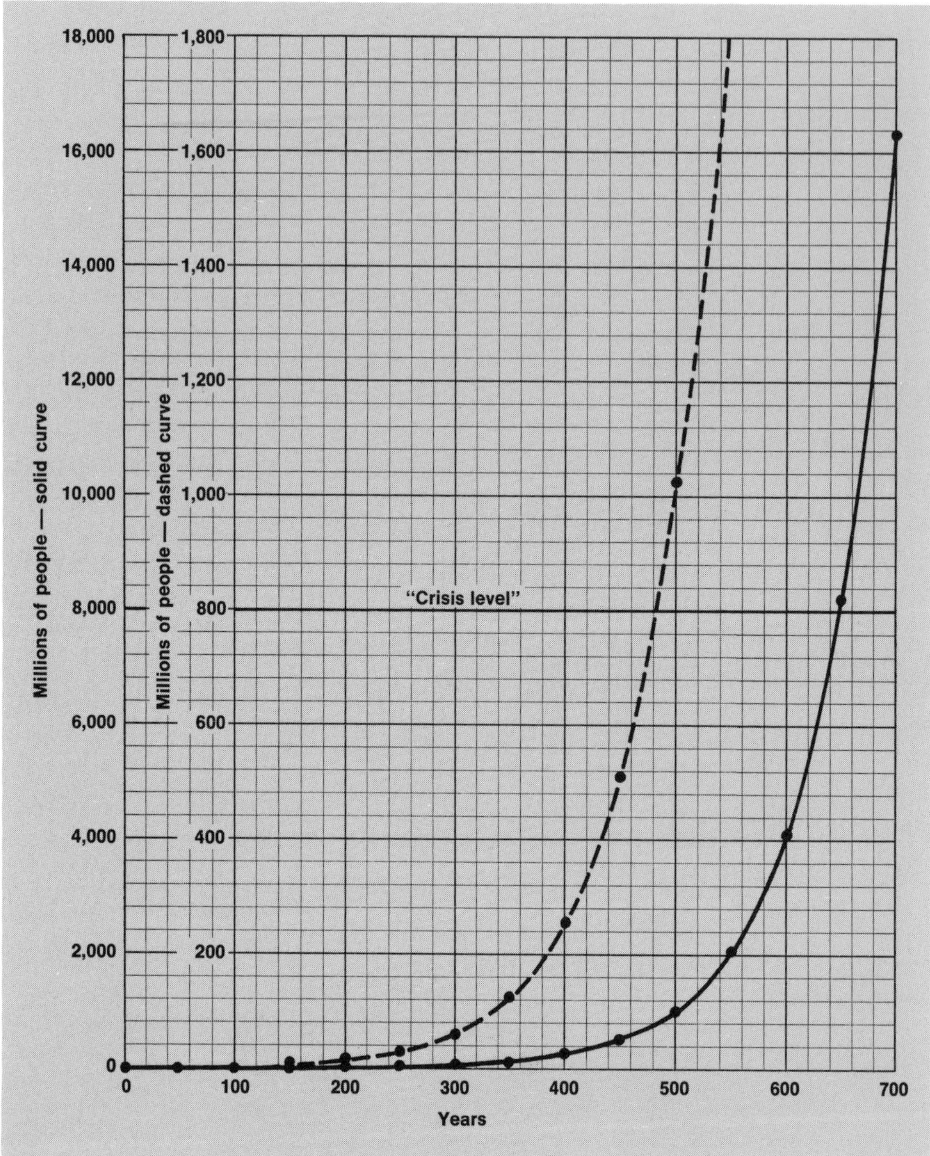

Figure 1-2 Population growth, plotted to scale, with a doubling time of 50 years.

collision that force awareness of processes that have long existed but have been ignored. Not until the 600th year in Figure 1-2 did population reach half of the crisis level. During all earlier time, growth would have seemed desirable and unhampered by physical limitations. Then suddenly in one more 50-year interval, in a mere instant of history, the upward-thrusting curve crosses the crisis level. In less than one lifetime, all traditions and expectations are shattered. This happens even though nothing has changed in the underlying law which until then has governed growth. Population, which doubled 12 times in the preceding 600 years, only doubles twice more between the 600th and the 700th years. But in this one century it becomes apparent that 50-year doubling cannot continue as the rule controlling growth.

Within one lifetime, dormant forces within the world system can exert themselves and take control. Falling food supply, rising pollution, and decreasing space per person are on the verge of combining to generate pressures great enough to reduce birth rate and increase death rate. When ultimate limits are approached, negative forces in the system gather strength until they stop the growth processes that had previously been in control. In one brief moment of time the world finds that the apparent law of exponential growth fails as the complete description of nature. Other fundamental laws of nature and the social system have been lying in wait until their time has come. Forces within the world system must and will rise far enough to suppress the power of growth.

1.2 Transition into Equilibrium

This book examines some of the forces that will become barriers when growth goes too far. It examines the changes that can arise to stop exponential growth. It begins to examine the transition from a world of growth to a world in equilibrium.

It is surprising enough, as in Figure 1-2, when exponential growth suddenly thrusts against fixed limits beyond which it cannot penetrate. But system pressures usually arise even more suddenly than implied by the exponential curve of Figure 1-2. Very often, relationships are such that exponential growth encounters shrinking space. The clash is thereby accentuated. Consider, as an example, a population that is expanding into a fixed geographical space. Suppose that each person requires one unit of land for "occupancy space." Occupancy space is the land for housing, commercial activity, transportation, and pollution dissipation. Suppose also that for adequate nourishment each person requires two units of land for food production. In this simple example, no account is taken of variable quality of land or of changing agricultural productivity.

If occupancy space is subtracted from the total land, the remainder gives the land available for agriculture. The agricultural land per person can be interpreted to give the adequacy of food supply as assumed in Figure 1-3. A position along the horizontal axis corresponds to the agricultural land units per person that remain after occupancy space is subtracted. The vertical axis gives the ratio of the food per person to that needed for adequate nourishment. For example, if there are 2 agricultural land units per person, the corresponding point on the curve shows a food ratio of 1.0, which is just sufficient. At 4 units of land per person, the food ratio is shown as 1.3. But food per person does not rise with greater availability of land per person, for the food is not needed and the labor is not available to grow crops. Toward the left-hand side of the diagram, as land per person declines, the adequacy of food supply falls rapidly, reaching zero if there is no agricultural land remaining.

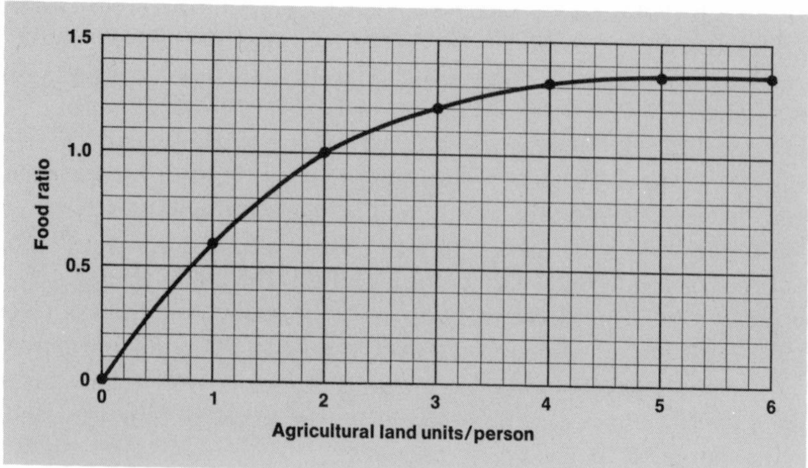

Figure 1-3 Food ratio (adequacy) as it depends on agricultural land units per person.

Figure 1-3 presents an assumption about how the food per person is related to the agricultural land per person. Only the general shape is important here. The curve asserts at the left end that zero land produces zero food. At the right end it recognizes that additional food per person rapidly decreases in utility as food exceeds the amount needed. The figure relates a physical variable (land per person) to a satisfaction or quality of life concept (adequacy of food supply). In a larger system, food ratio would be a factor in determining birth rate and average life span. The figure illustrates the numerous concepts that tie together a system of multiple sectors. Many relationships of this type are discussed in Chapter 3 to interconnect the demographic, industrial, agricultural, resource extraction, and pollution sectors of the world system.

Figure 1-4 shows the same population, doubling each 50 years, as in Figure 1-1. Population is here assumed to be growing into a space of 24,000 million land units. The third column gives the land units needed for occupancy at the rate of 1 unit per person. The fourth column shows the land remaining for agriculture from the total of 24,000 million units. The fifth column gives the land units per person available for growing food. The last column is the food ratio taken from Figure 1-3 corresponding to each value of land availability in the preceding column. During the first 600 years, while population is rising by a factor of 4,000, agricultural land declines by only 17%, and the food ratio is essentially constant at its maximum value. But in the next 100 years, population rises further by only another factor of four while agricultural land declines further by 62%. For the first time, occupancy land is encroaching on land that is needed for food. Population is rising and, at the "crisis level," begins to cause the agricultural land to shrink rapidly.

The food ratio versus time from Figure 1-4 is shown in Figure 1-5. For all of recorded time the ratio had been adequate, and then, in less than one lifetime, it

Years	Millions of people	Occupancy land units, millions	Agricultural land units, millions	Agricultural land units per person	Food ratio
0	1	1	23,999	23,999	1.35
50	2	2	23,998	11,999	1.35
100	4	4	23,996	5,999	1.35
150	8	8	23,992	2,999	1.35
200	16	16	23,984	1,499	1.35
250	32	32	23,968	749	1.35
300	64	64	23,936	374	1.35
350	128	128	23,872	187	1.35
400	256	256	23,744	93	1.35
450	512	512	23,488	46	1.35
500	1,024	1,024	22,976	22	1.35
550	2,048	2,048	21,952	10.72	1.35
600	4,096	4,096	19,904	4.86	1.34
620	5,405	5,405	18,595	3.44	1.26
640	7,132	7,132	16,868	2.37	1.09
660	9,410	9,410	14,590	1.55	0.85
680	12,417	12,417	11,583	0.93	0.57
700	16,384	16,384	7,616	0.46	0.30

Figure 1-4 People, space, and food ratio with a fixed land area of 24 billion units and a population doubling time of 50 years.

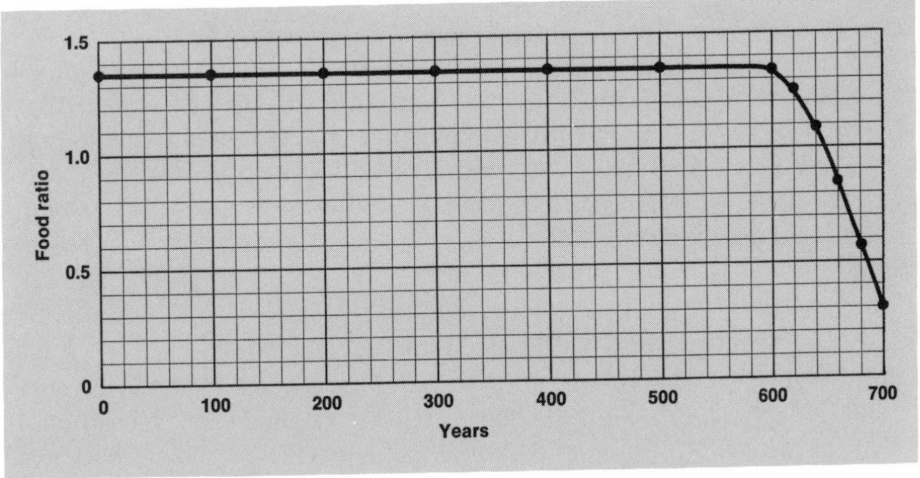

Figure 1-5 The food ratio (food adequacy) which has been potentially sufficient throughout all of history suddenly, within a span of 40 years, falls to a starvation crisis due to the simultaneous rise in population and decline in agricultural land.

precipitously drops low enough that food becomes a limit to further growth in population.

In the United States, urbanization is encroaching rapidly on farm land. Agricultural land is nearly all utilized; the untapped reservoir is nearly exhausted. Rural land in New Jersey and California is reported to be disappearing into housing developments and industrial use at the rate of several thousand acres per month. Since 1945 about half the farm land in New Jersey, the Garden State, has been lost. The disappearance of farm land has been masked by rising productivity per unit area obtained by farm mechanization, irrigation, pesticides, and improved varieties of plants. But these cannot continue without limit. As the processes of Figures 1-4 and 1-5 take effect, the agricultural surplus available for export will decline. After the export buffer has been diverted to internal use, the full significance of Figure 1-5 will become apparent. For decades the United States has tried to cope with its "farm surplus" problem. The traditional concern about surplus can obscure the arrival of a shortage until it is too late to redirect the forces of growth into a satisfactory form of long-term equilibrium.

The abruptness seen in Figures 1-4 and 1-5 might not be so accentuated in real life because land is of varying quality, starvation pressures cause more intensive use of land, and population increase would be slowed gradually to keep the food ratio from falling as low as shown in the figures where population is assumed to continue growing unchecked.

But the combination of expanding population with shrinking environment is a general phenomenon with broader implications than for food supply alone. As population rises, the rate of usage of natural resources increases, and the remaining store of resources shrinks to collide with the rising demand. Rising industrialization causes an increase in pollution generation, but pollution itself may poison the pollution-cleanup processes in nature so that increased generation of pollution clashes with a falling ability of the environment to dissipate pollution.

This book examines the structure of countervailing forces at the world level when growth overloads the environment. The world will encounter one of several possible alternative futures depending on whether population growth is eventually suppressed by shortage of natural resources, by pollution, by crowding and consequent social strife, or by insufficient food. Malthus dealt only with the latter, but it is possible for civilization to fall victim to other pressures before the food shortage occurs.

It is certain that resource shortage, pollution, crowding, food failure, or some other equally powerful force will limit population and industrialization if persuasion and psychological factors do not. Exponential growth cannot continue forever. Our greatest immediate challenge is how we guide the transition from growth to equilibrium. There are many possible mechanisms of growth suppression. That some one or combination will occur is inevitable. Unless we come to understand and to choose, the social system by its internal processes will choose for us. The internal mechanisms for terminating exponential growth appear highly undesirable. Unless we understand and act soon, we may be overwhelmed by a social and economic system we have created but cannot control.

1.3 Preview

This section summarizes results and tentative conclusions from Chapters 4, 5, and 6. The interpretations are based on behavior of the computer model developed in Chapter 3. The model is derived from statements, observations, and

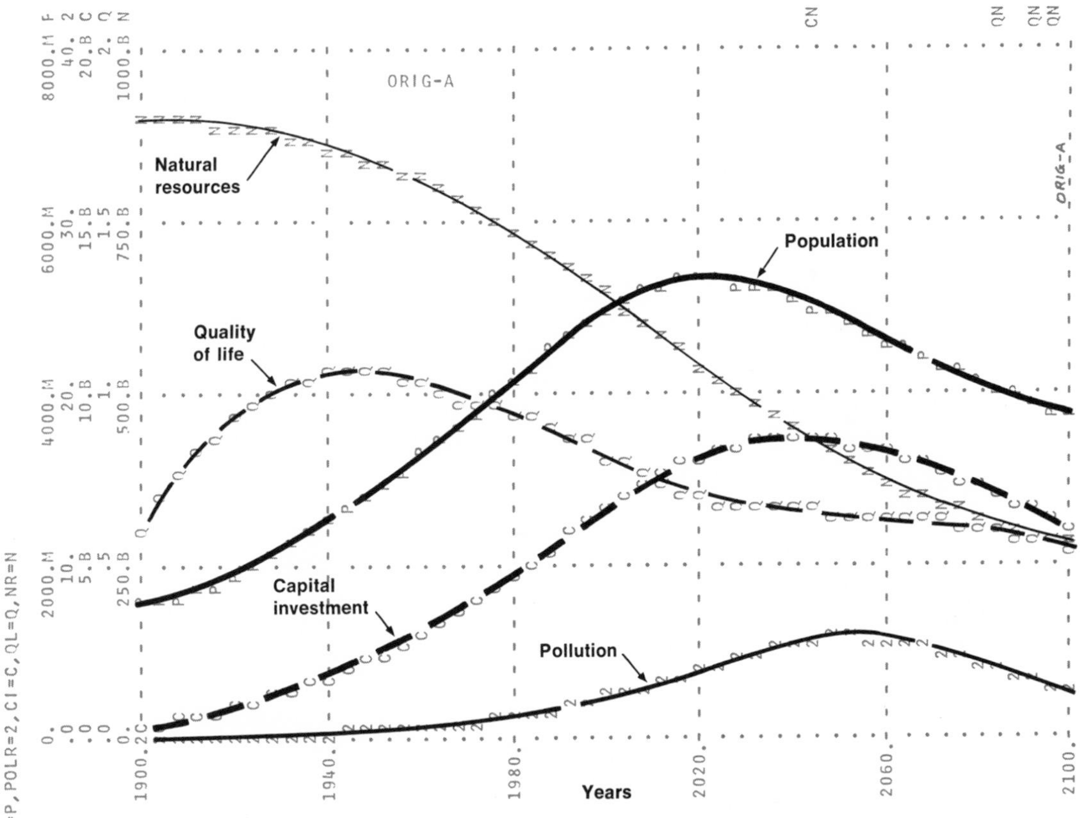

Figure 1-6 Population decline imposed by depletion of natural resources.

assumptions about the world system. The computer model interconnects concepts from demography, economics, agriculture, and technology. The model describes a world system that shows a variety of alternative behaviors. Which behavior is the most likely scenario for the future depends on policies that man may still be able to choose.

The world system can exhibit many alternate modes of behavior in response to different policies that man might follow in guiding population growth, capital investment generation, natural-resource usage, pollution control, and agricultural output. Figure 1-6, discussed more fully in Chapter 4, illustrates one possible future. Here population and capital investment grow until natural resources decline far enough to inhibit expansion. As resources decline still further, the world is unable to sustain the peak population. Population then declines along with capital investment. Quality of life depends on material standard of living, food supply, crowding, and pollution. Quality of life in Figure 1-6 falls because of the pressures created by the shortage of natural resources. Further explanation will be found in Chapter 4.

But the depletion of natural resources may not be the first and most likely

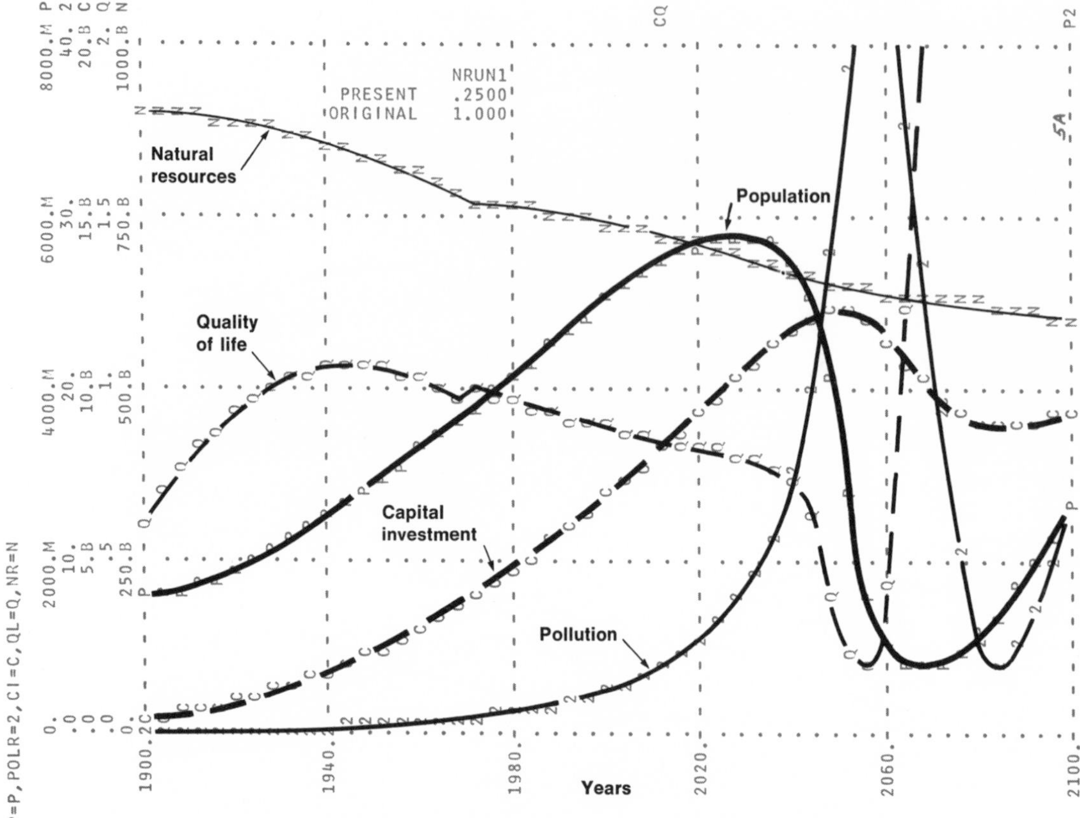

Figure 1-7 Pollution crisis triggered by reducing the usage rate of natural resources by 75% in 1970.

pressure to limit the growth of population. The world today seems to be entering a condition in which pressures are rising simultaneously from every one of the influences that can suppress growth—depleted resources, pollution, crowding, and insufficient food. It is still unclear which will dominate if mankind continues along the present path. The gradual peaking and decline of population in Figure 1-6 is less traumatic than other paths into equilibrium that the world system may exhibit.

Instead of allowing a limit to growth to be imposed by declining resources, science may very well find ways to use the more plentiful metals and to increase our sources of energy so that resource depletion does not intervene. If so, the way then remains open for growth until some other pressure arises within the system. Figure 1-7 shows the result when the resource shortage is foreseen and avoided. Here the only change from the conditions of Figure 1-6 is in the usage rate of natural resources after the year 1970. In Figure 1-7 after 1970, resources are assumed to be expended at only 25% of the rate assumed in Figure 1-6. In other words, to see whether a more desirable future is created, we assume that technology sustains the standard of living with a lower drain on the expendable and irreplaceable resources.

But the picture becomes even less attractive. If resources hold out, Figure 1-7 shows population and capital investment rising until a pollution crisis is created. Pollution then acts directly to reduce birth rate, increase death rate, and to depress food production. Population, which according to this simple model peaks at the year 2030, has fallen to one-sixth of its highest level within an interval of 20 years. Such a plunge would be a world-wide catastrophe. Should it occur, one can speculate on which sectors of the world population would suffer most. It is quite possible that the more industrialized countries, from which the pollution comes, would be the least able to survive such a disruption to environment and food supply. They might be the ones to take the brunt of the collapse. There is now developing a strong undercurrent of doubt about technology as the savior of mankind. There is a basis for such doubt. We see in Figure 1-7 how one technological success (reducing our dependence on natural resources) can merely save us from one fate only to make us the victims of something worse (a pollution catastrophe).

The following issues are raised by the dynamic behavior shown by the model of world forces. These preliminary interpretations need to be examined more deeply and confirmed by more thorough research into the assumptions about structure and detail of the world system. As described in the Preface, a major research program in the dynamics of world interactions is continuing under the sponsorship of The Club of Rome. Further work may well alter the present implications and emphasis and is sure to develop new insights and clarification.

1. Industrialization may be a more fundamental disturbing force in world ecology than is population. In fact, the population explosion is perhaps best viewed as a result of technology and industrialization. (Medicine and public health are included here as a part of industrialization.)

2. Within the next century, man may face choices from a four-pronged dilemma—suppression of modern industrial society by a natural-resource shortage; decline of world population from changes wrought by pollution; population limitation by food shortage; or population collapse from war, disease, and social stresses caused by physical and psychological crowding.

3. We may now be living in a "golden age" when, in spite of a widely acknowledged feeling of malaise, the quality of life is, on the average, higher than ever before in history and higher now than the future offers.

4. Exhortations and programs directed at population control may be inherently self-defeating. If population control begins to result, as hoped, in higher per capita food supply and material standard of living, these very im-

provements may relax the pressures and generate forces to trigger a resurgence of population growth.

5. The high standard of living of modern industrial societies seems to result from a production of food and material goods that has been able to outrun the rising population. But, as agriculture reaches a space limit, as industrialization reaches a natural-resource limit, and as both reach a pollution limit, population tends to catch up. Population then grows until the "quality of life" falls far enough to stabilize population.

6. There may be no realistic hope of the present underdeveloped countries reaching the standard of living demonstrated by the present industrialized nations. The pollution and natural-resource load placed on the world environmental system by each person in an advanced country is probably 20 to 50 times greater than the load now generated by a person in an underdeveloped country. With 4 times as many people in underdeveloped countries as in the present developed countries, their rising to the economic level that has been set as a standard by the industrialized nations could mean an increase of 10 times in the natural-resource and pollution load on the world environment. Noting the destruction that has already occurred on land, in the air, and especially in the oceans, capability appears not to exist for handling such a rise in standard of living. In fact, the present disparity between the developed and underdeveloped nations may be equalized as much by a decline in the developed countries as by an improvement in the underdeveloped countries.

7. A society with a high level of industrialization may be nonsustainable. It may be self-extinguishing if it exhausts the natural resources on which it depends. Or, if unending substitution for declining natural resources were possible, a new international strife over pollution and environmental rights might pull the average world-wide standard of living back to the level of a century ago.

8. From the long view of a hundred years hence, the present efforts of underdeveloped countries to industrialize may be unwise. They may now be closer to an ultimate equilibrium with the environment than are the industrialized

nations. The present underdeveloped countries may be in a better condition for surviving forthcoming world-wide environmental and economic pressures than are the advanced countries. If one of the several forces strong enough to cause a collapse in world population does arise, the underdeveloped countries might suffer far less than their share of the decline because economies with less organization, integration, and specialization are probably less vulnerable to disruption.

1.4 Background

At the Massachusetts Institute of Technology over the last 40 years there has developed a powerful approach to understanding the dynamics of complex systems. The foundation was laid in the 1930's when Vannevar Bush built his differential analyzer to solve the equations of certain simple engineering problems. Such a set of equations is a model of the system they represent. Such a model describes the rules that govern the system behavior. The differential analyzer, set up in accordance with the equations that are the instructions, becomes a simulator to trace the dynamic behavior of the system being studied. In that same period Norbert Wiener developed his concepts of feedback systems that were later given the name "cybernetics." Harold L. Hazen wrote some of the first introductory papers in the field of feedback control that was to be known as "servomechanisms." In the 1940's Gordon S. Brown created the Servomechanisms Laboratory in which the theory of feedback systems was expanded, recorded, taught, and radiated. In the 1950's Jay W. Forrester, author of this book, was director of the Digital Computer Laboratory and Division 6 of the Lincoln Laboratory where digital computers were first used for system simulators; and, since 1956, he and a group of associates at the M.I.T. Alfred P. Sloan School of Management have extended the preceding developments to cope with the greater complexity of social systems.

The philosophy and method of the approach used here were described in *Industrial Dynamics* (1961, Reference 2). *Principles of Systems* (1968, Reference 3) presents the theory of structure in dynamic systems, and *Urban Dynamics* (1969, Reference 5) is an application to growth and decline of a city. For several years, the modeling of the feedback-loop structure of social systems has been known as "industrial dynamics," but the name has become a misnomer now that applications are becoming important outside the industrial corporation. Because the methods apply to complex systems wherever we find them, a better name is "system dynamics." Applications have been made to corporate policy, to dynamics of diabetes as a medical system, to social forces affecting drug addiction in a community, to the dynamics of commodity markets, and to the behavior of research and development organizations. (See References 4, 6, 7, and 11.)

Out of this background, an invitation was extended to the Executive Committee of The Club of Rome to visit M.I.T. for two weeks to review the system dynamics program and to evaluate the applicability to the Club's project on world evolution. The invitation was accepted, and a conference was held beginning July 20, 1970.*

From several years of teaching the dynamics of social systems, we have observed that mere description of the process of model formulation and computer simulation is not an effective form of teaching. The student must participate. He must do and experience each step. For this reason, workshop sessions were included in the afternoons of the July conference. But another characteristic has also become evident about newcomers to the study of social dynamics. Most are not at first able to visualize the transfer of method from one field of application to another. To avoid the difficulty of transfer, it seemed necessary to have a workshop vehicle that dealt with the problem area of interest to The Club of Rome. The world model described in the following chapters was created to be the basis for the workshop sessions of the conference.

1.5 Mental Models of Social Systems

There is nothing new in the use of models to represent social systems. Everyone uses models all the time. Every person in his private life and in his community life uses models for decision making. The mental image of the world around one, carried in each individual's head, is a model. One does not have a family, a business, a city, a government, or a country in his head. He has only selected concepts and relationships which he uses to represent the real system. A mental image is a model. All of our decisions are taken on the basis of models. All of our laws are passed on the basis of models. All executive actions are taken on the basis of models. The question is not whether to use or ignore models. The question is only a choice between alternative models.

The mental model is fuzzy. It is incomplete. It is imprecisely stated. Furthermore, even within one individual, the mental model changes with time and with the flow of conversation. The human mind assembles a few relationships to fit the context of a discussion. As the subject shifts, so does the model. Even as a single topic is being discussed, each participant in a conversation is using a different mental model through which to interpret the subject. Fundamental assumptions differ but are never brought into the open. Goals are different and are left unstated. It is little wonder that compromise takes so long. And it is not surprising that consensus leads to actions which produce unintended results.

The human mind selects a few perceptions, which may be right or wrong, and uses these as a description of the world around us. On the basis of these assumptions a person estimates the system behavior that he believes is implied. If he desires an improved behavior, he judges what action might be taken to alter the system. But this process is often faulty.

*This symposium was funded by the Volkswagen Foundation (Stiftung Volkswagenwerk).

The human mind is excellent in its ability to observe the elementary forces and actions of which a system is composed. The human mind is effective in identifying the structure of a complex situation. But human experience trains the mind only poorly for estimating the dynamic consequences of how the parts of a system will interact with one another.

Until recently there has been no way to estimate the behavior of social systems except by contemplation, discussions, argument, and guesswork.

1.6 Computer Models of Social Systems

The approach used here to examine the world system combines the strength of the human mind with the strength of today's computers. The human is best able to perceive the pressures, fears, goals, habits, prejudices, delays, resistance to change, dedication, good will, greed, and other human characteristics that control the individual facets of our social systems. Only the human mind seems at present able to formulate a structure into which separate scraps of information can be fitted. But when the pieces of the system have been assembled, the mind is nearly useless for anticipating the dynamic behavior that the system implies. Here the computer is ideal. It will trace the interactions of any specified set of relationships without doubt or error.

The computer is instructed by giving it a model. A model is a set of descriptions that tell the computer how each part of the system acts. It is now possible to construct realistic laboratory models of social systems. Such a model is a simplification of an actual social system, but it can be far more comprehensive than the mental models we otherwise would use as the basis for debating social policy.

A computer model embodies a theory of system structure. It states assumptions about the system. The model is only as good as the theory which lies behind it. A good computer model is distinguished from a poor one because it captures more of the essence of the social system that it presumes to represent. Making a computer model requires that we be explicit about the assumptions on which our mental models are based. When assumptions are clearly stated, they encourage deeper discussion and lead to better selections from the vast numbers of fragments which are contained in our mental models. Making a computer model enforces a rigor and discipline that is missing in discussion and writing.

While none of the computer models of social systems existing today can be considered more than preliminary, many are now beginning to show the behavior characteristics of actual systems. These models explain why we are having our present difficulties and furthermore explain why so many efforts to improve social systems have failed. In spite of their shortcomings, models can now be constructed that are far superior to the intuitive models on which we are currently basing our future survival.

Given the assumptions about how different parts of a complex system affect each other, the computer can then trace the operation of the system through time. It can carry through the arithmetic tasks and follow the rules of behavior as set down in the model description. The computer gives the correct implications of the assumptions that went into the construction of the model. This process of modeling combines the greatest strength of the human mind, its ability to perceive the surrounding world, and eliminates the greatest weakness of the human mind, its inability to estimate the dynamic consequences of even a correct set of system assumptions. Chapters 2 and 3 illustrate the process of going from ordinary, reasonable assumptions about the world system to a computer model that interrelates those assumptions. The computer then shows, as discussed in Chapters 4, 5, and 6, the unexpected consequences that can lie within the assumptions.

2 Structure of the World System

Suggestions to the reader: This chapter gives an overview of the structure chosen to represent interactions between the major sectors of the world system. Section 2.1 introduces the complete system while the following sections identify major substructures that generate growth forces and equilibrium pressures. Chapter 2 should be read for general impressions and not for details. Chapter 3 contains the full detail and assumptions of the computer model. Almost all of the concepts and numerical values used in this chapter will be explained more fully in Chapter 3.

In constructing a computer model of a social system, the selection and arrangement of information about the real system is crucial. Generally we are handicapped not so much by a shortage of information as by an excess of information from which to choose. Not only is there far more information available than it is appropriate to include, but also the information is unstructured. The unrelated fragments of information must be organized. Organizing the information yields the structure of the model. Formation of the model should be guided by the principles of structure that are common to all dynamic systems. A summary of some basic principles of system structure may be helpful to the reader.

The most important concept in establishing the structure of a system is the idea that all actions take place within "feedback loops." The feedback loop is the closed path that connects an action to its effect on the surrounding conditions, and these resulting conditions in turn come back as "information" to influence further action. We often erroneously think of cause and effect as flowing in only one direction. We speak of action A causing result B. But such a perception is incomplete. Result B represents a new condition of the system that changes the future influences that affect action at A.

Feedback loops govern action and change in systems from the simplest to the most complex. As an example, one's condition of weariness causes adjustment in the length of time devoted to sleep, sleep changes the state of weariness, and the new degree of weariness further adjusts the time for sleep. There is a closed-loop structure between action (sleeping) and the system condition (weariness) that in turn affects the action. All the processes of growth and equilibrium are generated within feedback loops. Examples relative to the world model will be discussed in later sections.

Within the feedback loops of a system, the principles of system structure tell us that two kinds of variables will be found–levels and rates. The levels are the accumulations (integrations) within the system. The rates are the flows that cause the levels to change.

A level accumulates the net quantity that results from the flow rates that add to and subtract from the level. The system levels fully describe the state or condition of a system at any point in time. One's bank balance is a system level; it is created by accumulating the net difference between the money flows in and out. In financial accounting statements, the level variables are those found on the balance sheet, whereas those on the profit and loss statement represent system rates. Levels exist in all subsystems–financial, physical, biological, psychological, and economic. Population, created by accumulating the net difference between birth rate and death rate, would be a level of the world system. Levels are caused to change only by the related rates of flow.

A rate of flow is controlled only by one or more of the system levels and not by other rates. All systems that change through time can be represented by using only levels and rates. The two kinds of variables are necessary but at the same time sufficient for representing any system. Full explanation of these and other principles of structure and the principles of the dynamics of behavior lie beyond the present scope but can be found elsewhere (References 2 and 3).

The system dynamicist starts most effectively from intensive discussions with a group of people who know the system first-hand. Such people should be active participants in the social system. They should speak from a variety of backgrounds and viewpoints so opinions will clash. The atmosphere of the discussion should require that conflicting opinion be at least partially resolved, for it is by that process that the underlying assumptions are most quickly revealed.

During such a discussion, the dynamicist gleans the fragments of information from which he assembles a model that captures the essential structure of the system. Some of the information describes cause-effect chains. Other information identifies system levels.

2.1 System Diagram

The model described in this chapter and the next was chosen to represent the system of interest to The Club of Rome. It grew out of a meeting in Bern, Switzerland on June 29, 1970 and from my own background of experience and reading. The model is preliminary. Its purpose is to raise questions and to trigger further work. In the latter it has already been effective. Under the auspices of The Club of Rome and financed by a grant from the Volkswagen Foundation (Stiftung Volkswagenwerk) a major project, directed by Professor Dennis Meadows at M.I.T., was established to review the assumptions and structure. A revised world model is now being generated in a program that includes extensive discussion with many groups that are working with the separate sectors of the world system. It is especially important to review, revise, and document the structure of the model system because structure is usually more important than the assumed numerical values in determining the modes of behavior that a system can exhibit.

Five levels were chosen as the cornerstones on which to build the system structure:

Population
Capital investment
Natural resources
Fraction of capital devoted to agriculture
Pollution

Each of these levels represents the principal variable in a major subsystem of world structure. The five levels interact in multiple ways. The entire structure is shown in Figure 2-1. (See also the removable duplicate diagram inside the back cover of the book.)

In the figure, the system levels appear as the rectangles. Each level is increased or decreased by its associated rates of flow. An example of a flow is the valve symbol for birth rate in the upper left corner. In all systems, levels are caused to change only by rates of flow. Conversely, rates depend only on system levels through an information network as shown by the dashed lines and circles. A system structure consists only of levels and rates. The circles in the diagram are parts of the rate descriptions but have been separated from the rate symbols because they are concepts that are most clearly described independently. The irregular cloud symbols are sources or sinks for the flows and lie outside the system. For each symbol in the figure there is a name, a letter group as an abbreviation, and a number. The number is the number of the corresponding equation in Appendix B and in the subsection numbering of Chapter 3. The letter groups are the abbreviations used in the equations of Chapter 3 and Appendix B.

In a flow diagram such as Figure 2-1, any closed path through the diagram is a feedback loop. Such a path must be chosen to follow the direction of the arrows along the dashed information lines but need not follow the direction of arrows for the flows controlled by the system rates. Some of the closed loops will, under some circumstances, be "positive-feedback loops" that generate growth in the system. Other loops, usually the majority, will be "negative-feedback loops" that seek an equilibrium.

2.2 Population Loops

Figure 2-2 shows the two fundamental loops that affect population. The upper loop generates new births that add to population. The lower loop creates the death rate that depletes population. Here "birth rate" and "death rate" are measured in people per year. They represent the total rate at which population is being increased and decreased. The coefficients BRN and DRN are equivalent to

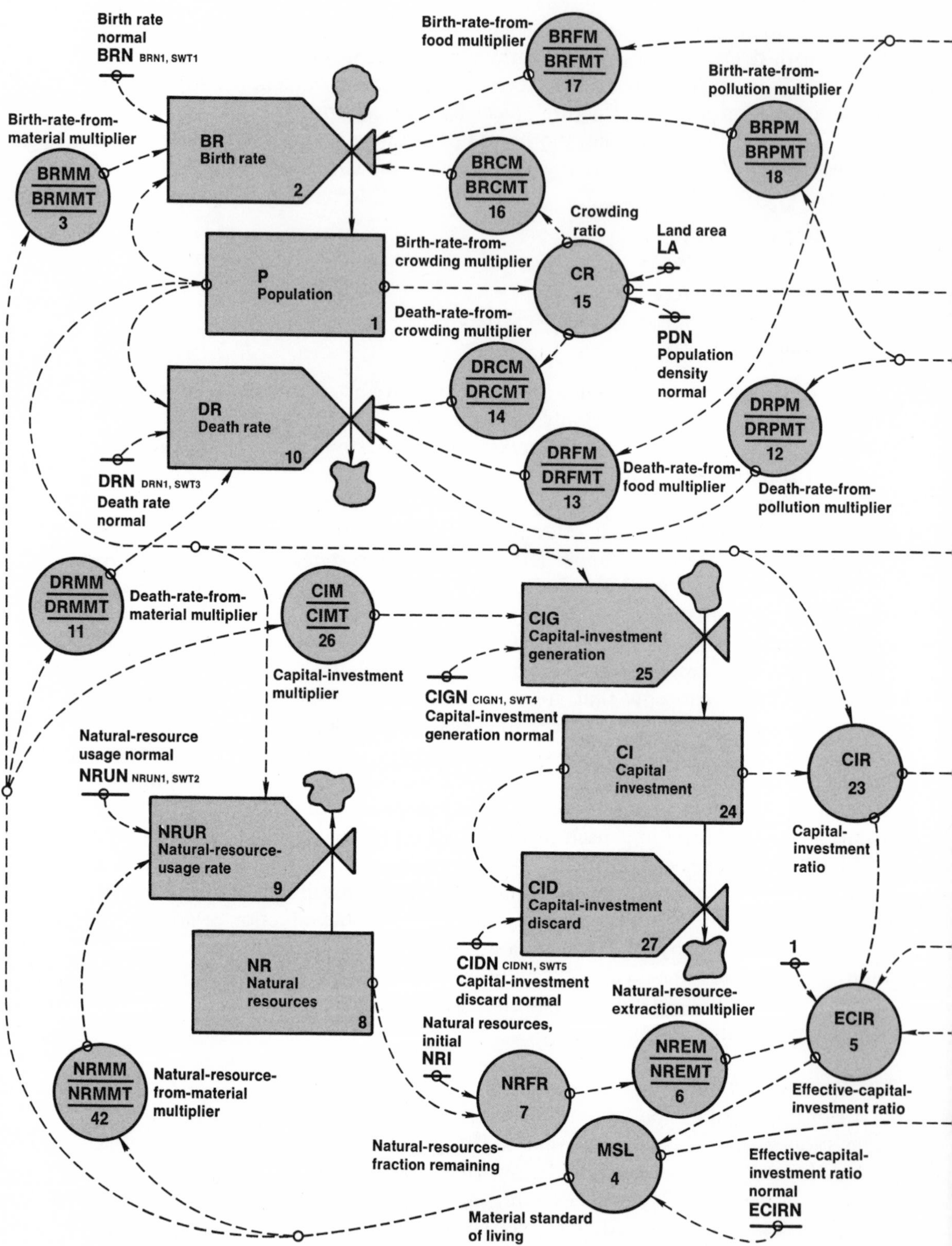

Figure 2-1 Complete diagram of the world model interrelating the five level variables — population, natural resources, capital investment, capital-investment-in-agriculture fraction, and pollution.

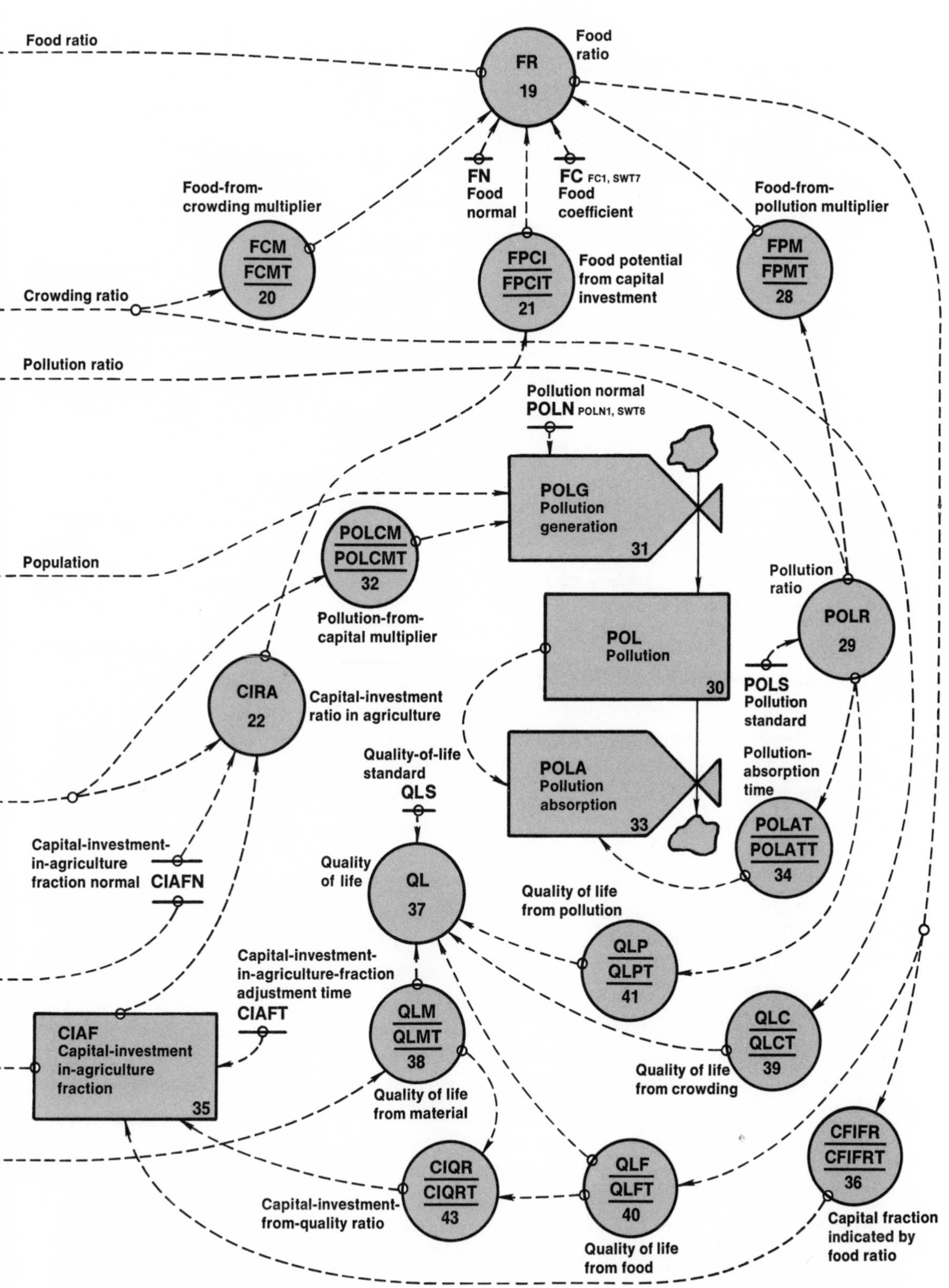

Food ratio
FR
19
Food
ratio
FN
Food
normal
FC FC1, SWT7
Food
coefficient
Food-from-
crowding multiplier
FCM
FCMT
20
FPCI
FPCIT
21
Food potential
from capital
investment
Food-from-
pollution multiplier
FPM
FPMT
28
Crowding ratio
Pollution ratio
Pollution normal
POLN POLN1, SWT6
POLG
Pollution
generation
31
POLCM
POLCMT
32
Population
Pollution-from-
capital multiplier
POL
Pollution
30
Pollution
ratio
POLR
29
POLS
Pollution
standard
CIRA
22
Capital-investment
ratio in agriculture
Quality-of-life
standard
QLS
POLA
Pollution
absorption
33
Pollution-
absorption
time
POLAT
POLATT
34
Capital-investment-
in-agriculture
fraction normal
CIAFN
Quality
of life
QL
37
Quality of life
from pollution
QLP
QLPT
41
Capital-investment-
in-agriculture-fraction
adjustment time
CIAFT
QLM
QLMT
38
QLC
QLCT
39
CIAF
Capital-investment
in-agriculture
fraction
35
Quality of life
from material
Quality of life
from crowding
CFIFR
CFIFRT
36
CIQR
CIQRT
43
QLF
QLFT
40
Capital-investment-
from-quality ratio
Quality of life
from food
Capital fraction
indicated by
food ratio

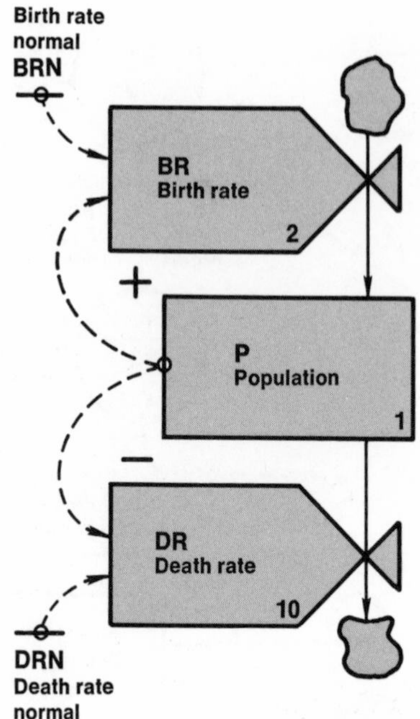

Figure 2-2 Basic birth and death loops in the population sector.

the normal use of the terms birth rate and death rate and are the fraction of the population that is born or dies each year. For example, the value of BRN is taken as 0.04 (40 per thousand) which is multiplied by population to determine birth rate BR. That is, under normal conditions, there is a 4% addition to the population each year from birth rate. At the same time, the coefficient DRN is 0.028 meaning that there is a 2.8% reduction of population each year due to death. The difference is a net increase of 1.2% per year. These rates are called "normal" rates because they correspond to a standard set of world conditions when the values of food, material standard of living, crowding, and pollution are all at their "standard" values. But these other system variables can change to cause birth and death rates to rise and fall from their normal values. The influences of these other conditions in the world system are introduced through "multipliers" that increase or decrease the normal system rates depending on how favorable or unfavorable the world environment may be at any particular time. It is through these multipliers that the condition of the world system, as reflected in food, material standard of living, crowding, and pollution, can cause population to increase, remain stable, or decline.

The birth loop in Figure 2-2 is positive feedback in character and generates population growth. An increase in population P causes, by way of the dashed information line, an increase in birth rate BR (number of people born in the system per year) which further increases the population P. (The capital letters refer to the abbreviations on the diagram.) Population increases birth rate which increases population, and the criteria for a positive-feedback loop are met. If there were no constraint to control it, population would increase forever according to the exponential growth pattern created by positive-feedback loops.

But the death loop is negative. As population grows, the number of annual deaths will grow also. An increase in population P, by way of the dashed line, increases death rate DR and *reduces* population P. Death rate here means the number of people who die per year.

The positive loop involving birth describes exponential growth and, if there were no deaths, would produce an upward-sweeping population as seen in Figure 1-2. If there were no births, the negative loop for death rate would generate a typical equilibrium-seeking behavior to cause population to decline toward zero. Taken together, the two loops can describe either exponential growth or decline toward zero, depending on which effect is stronger. As we will see, many other loops in the system are equilibrium-seeking toward a non-zero population and accomplish their mission by raising birth rate while at the same time lowering death rate or vice-versa. In a total system in equilibrium, population would be constant and would be maintained through system-induced opposing adjustments in both birth and death rates.

2.3 Capital-Investment Loops

Figure 2-3 pictures two of the loops that control capital investment. Again one is positive and one negative. Capital-investment generation CIG depends on population and on capital-investment generation normal CIGN, which states the capital units per person per year that will be generated under a "normal" condition for the material standard of living. But the capital-investment multiplier CIM modifies that normal rate of capital generation. At very low values of material standard of living, pressures to consume all output are so great that little capital can be accumulated. The ability to generate new capital increases as the amount of capital per person increases. However, at very high amounts of capital investment per person, there is reduced need and incentive for still more increase in the material standard of living, and the generation rate of new capital no longer rises with higher levels of capital.

Examining the positive loop in Figure 2-3, we see that an increase in capital investment CI increases the capital-investment ratio CIR that gives the capital investment per person, increases the effective-capital-investment ratio ECIR, increases the material standard of living MSL, increases the capital-investment multiplier CIM, increases capital-investment generation CIG, and increases capital investment CI. All the relationships reinforce growth; the loop is positive-feedback in character. In effect it says that capital investment produces capital investment. But, as already described, the capital-investment multiplier CIM ceases to rise at high values of total capital investment. A point can then be reached where the positive growth force of the loop declines enough that it no longer replaces the discard rate being generated by the negative loop involving capital investment CI

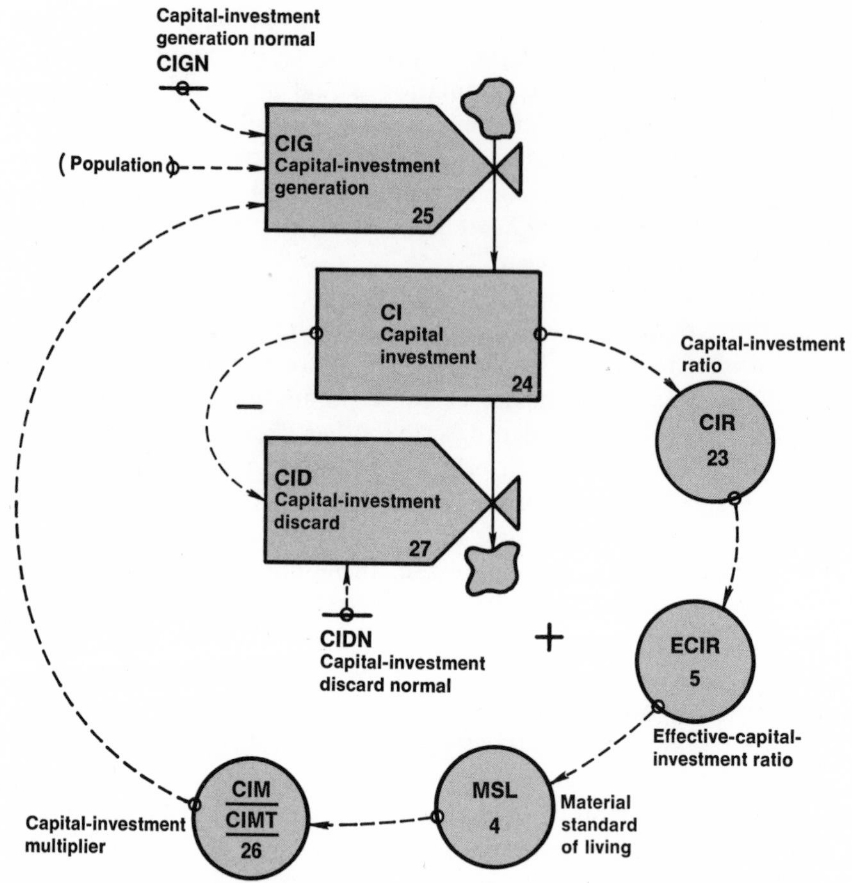

Figure 2-3 Positive loop in which capital produces capital and negative loop in which capital wears out and is discarded.

and the rate of capital-investment discard CID. In the negative loop capital-investment discard normal CIDN with a value of 0.025 gives the fraction of capital investment that wears out and is removed from the active stock each year. This is a 2.5% discard rate per year and is equivalent to an average life of 40 years for capital investment. These values are discussed more fully in Section 3.25.

2.4 Pollution Loops

Another positive-feedback loop exists in the pollution sector in conjunction with a negative loop as shown in Figure 2-4. The negative loop represents the basic pollution-absorption process. Of course, pollution must first exist if it is going to be dissipated. The more pollution that exists at any moment, the higher can be the rate of dissipation, as long as pollution is not high enough to depress the pollution-cleanup processes of nature. So pollution POL, if it increases, will increase pollution absorption POLA to *decrease* pollution. The reversal of effect

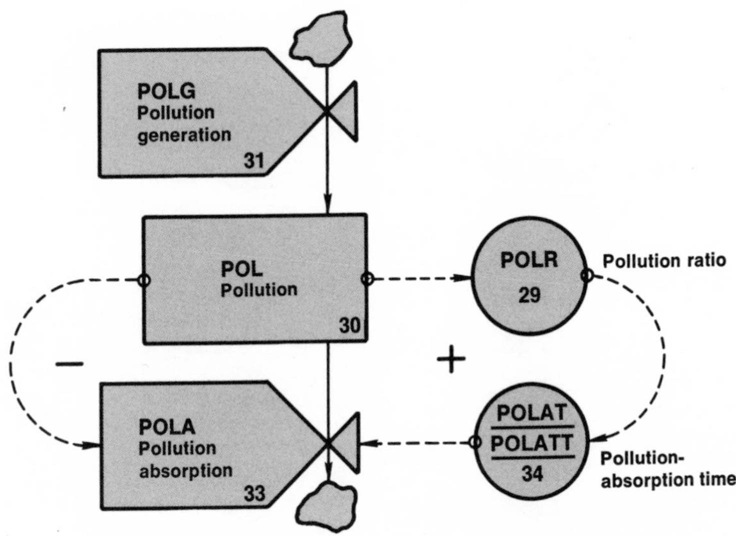

Figure 2-4 Negative loop controlling pollution absorption and positive loop that can cause regenerative accumulation of pollution.

defines a negative-feedback loop. The preceding simple description assumes that the time-constant of pollution absorption remains constant. (By defining values differently, one could speak of half-life which represents the same concept.) But the positive loop determines the time required for a fixed fraction of any existing pollution to be dissipated. Here the time-constant depends on the pollution load itself. When there is little pollution, pollution can be dissipated quickly. But rising pollution will poison and impede the cleanup processes and thereby increase the time constant of dissipation. In other words, the half-life is not constant as in spontaneous atomic decay. Assume there is an unchanging pollution input from pollution generation POLG. Then, looking at the positive loop in Figure 2-4, if pollution POL increases, the pollution ratio POLR increases, the pollution-absorption time POLAT increases; this *reduces* the rate of pollution absorption POLA, and tends to *increase* pollution POL. So an increase in pollution, traced around the loop, produces a still further increase, indicating a positive-feedback loop. The composite of the two loops can be either positive or negative depending on the range within which pollution lies. The run-away pollution catastrophes to follow in some of the computer runs in Chapter 4 are caused by the cumulative effect of this positive-feedback structure that occurs when total pollution becomes great enough so that absorption is depressed. Pollution-absorption time is discussed in Section 3.34.

2.5 Population Controlled by Crowding

The pair of negative loops in Figure 2-5 act to adjust population toward the amount of crowding that man can tolerate. Of course, the basic loops of Figure 2-2 are still present and active. The influences shown in Figure 2-5 alter the basic

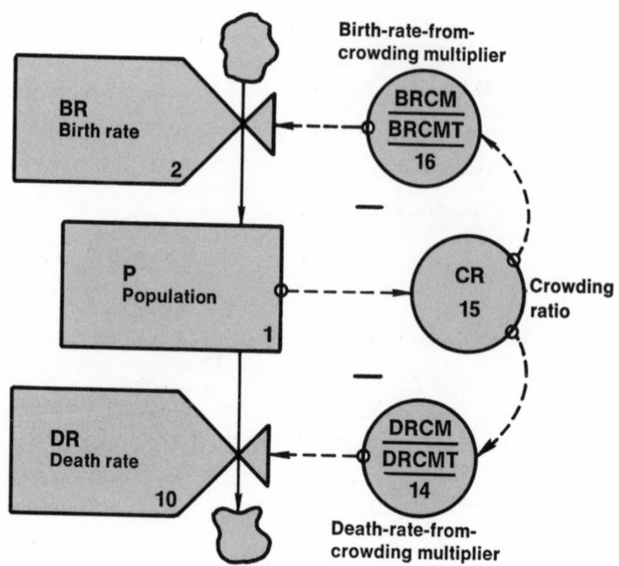

Figure 2-5 Negative loops that adjust crowding of population to the maximum density that man can psychologically tolerate.

birth and death rates. In the upper loop of Figure 2-5, if population P rises, crowding ratio CR increases, the birth-rate-from-crowding multiplier BRCM *declines,* birth rate BR is reduced, and population P is reduced. Likewise in the lower loop, if population P increases, the crowding ratio CR rises, the death-rate-from-crowding multiplier DRCM rises, the death rate DR rises, and this *reduces* population P. The double effect of reducing birth rate and increasing death rate can be a powerful stabilizer of population at the maximum tolerable value of crowding.

In a negative feedback loop, if more than one level variable is in the loop, the loop can become oscillatory and unstable. Such additional system levels will usually be present. Therefore, one would expect a more complete model to have additional level variables beyond the one shown in Figure 2-5. They might represent accumulating world tension or the momentum of war that could push population below the population-equilibrium level once a destructive process had started. The additional system levels could cause population overshoot and collapse instead of simple stabilization at the tolerable maximum population density.

2.6 Population Controlled by Food Supply

Figure 2-6 illustrates two negative loops that run through capital investment and food to regulate population in accordance with food supply. In the outer loop, if population P rises, capital investment ratio CIR *decreases,* capital investment ratio in agriculture CIRA decreases, food potential (per person) from capital investment FPCI decreases, food ratio FR decreases, birth-rate-from-food multiplier BRFM decreases, birth rate BR decreases, and population P decreases. The

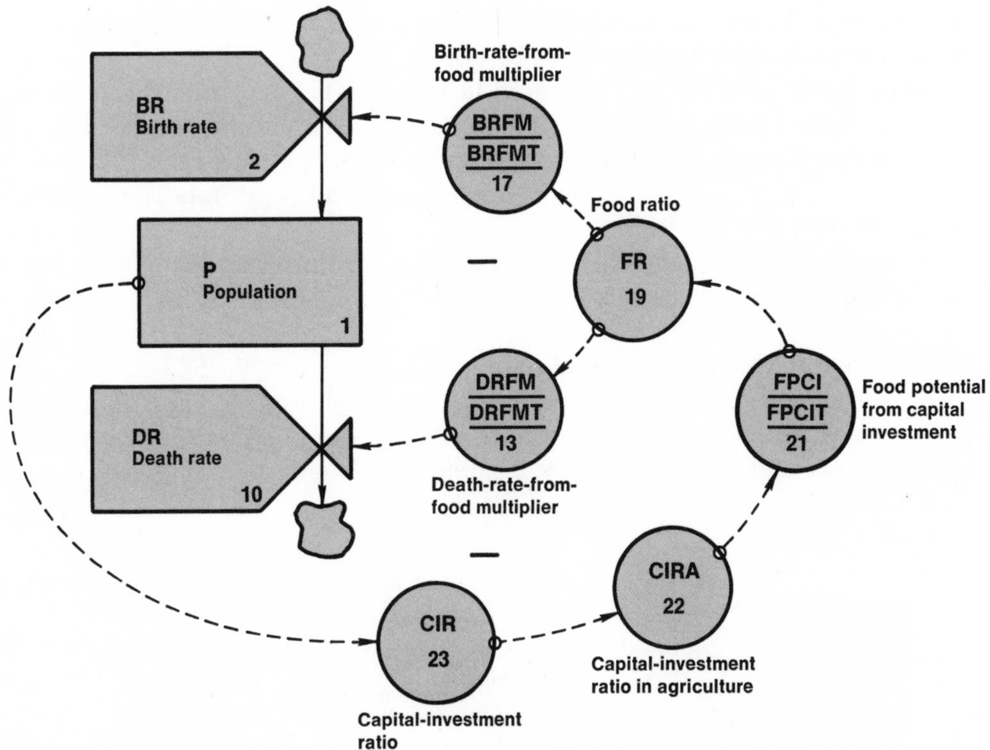

Figure 2-6 Negative loops that adjust population to the maximum that food can support.

reversal of impact—where a rise in population tends eventually to produce a downward influence on population—identifies a negative loop, one which is adjusting birth rate to regulate population in accordance with food supply. For the inner loop, if population P rises, capital investment ratio CIR *decreases,* capital investment ratio in agriculture CIRA decreases, food potential (per person) from capital investment FPCI decreases, food ratio FR decreases, death-rate-from-food multiplier DRFM *increases,* death rate DR increases, and population P *decreases.* Again, the impact of a population rise is reversed when it is traced around the circle, identifying a negative-feedback loop. This loop, by increasing death rate as food per capita decreases, also adjusts population to maintain balance with food supply.

It is no accident or coincidence that throughout history a substantial fraction of the world population has been undernourished and on the verge of starvation. The loops in Figure 2-6 regulate population so that population stays at that critical condition on the edge of starvation. In fact, the Malthusian thesis has been true and at work at all times. Population is regulated to the food supply. But thus far man has caused population to continue to increase by being able to push up the food supply. Increasing the total amount of food has done little in the long run to reduce the percentage of undernourished people. Instead, the larger the population generated by increased food supply, the greater the total number of people who live under the threat of starvation.

In a similar way, as can be traced in Figure 2-1, population P acts through crowding ratio CR to reduce the land available for agriculture as represented by the food-from-crowding multiplier FCM and reduces the food ratio FR. Then, as also occurred in Figure 2-6, birth rate is reduced and death rate is increased by multipliers BRFM and DRFM.

Crowding therefore acts directly on population through psychological effects (as in Figure 2-5) and indirectly through food (as in Figures 1-3, 1-4, and 1-5).

2.7 Population Controlled by Pollution

Under circumstances of high pollution and a high ratio of capital investment per capita, pollution becomes a strong regulator of population through the feedback loops of Figure 2-7. An increase in population P increases pollution generation

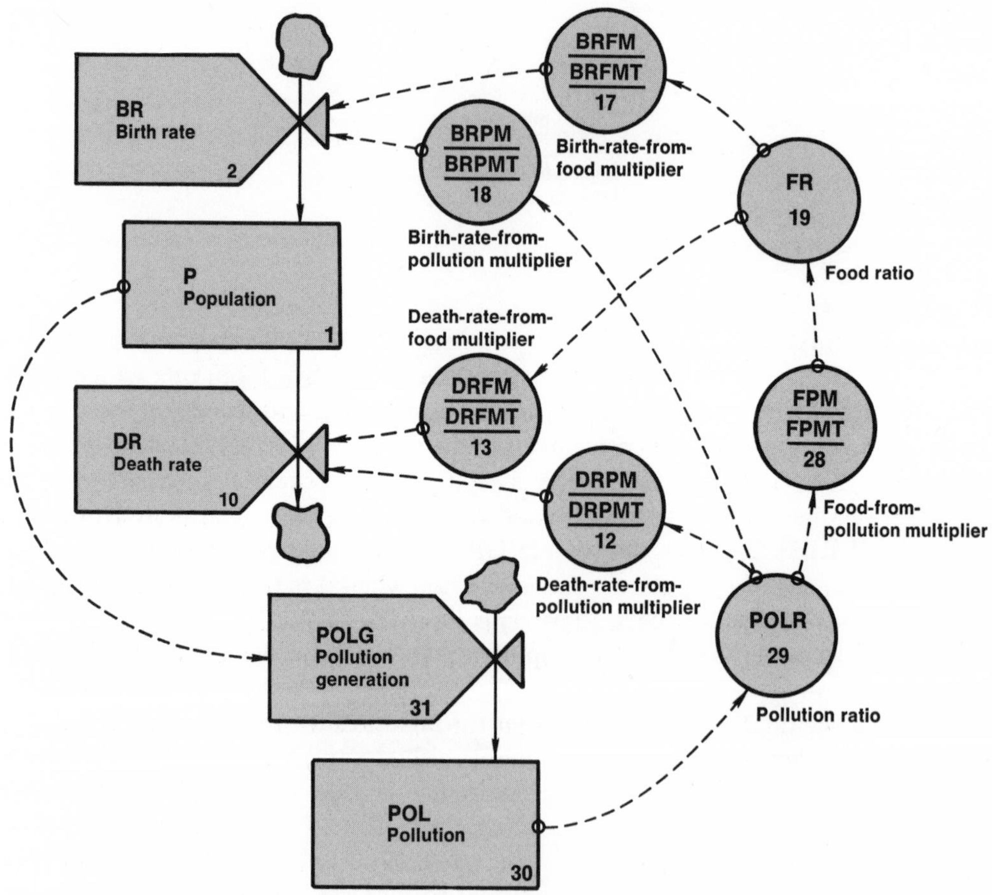

Figure 2-7 Negative loops that adjust population to the maximum number that can survive their own pollution.

POLG, increases pollution POL, and increases pollution ratio POLR. Through multipliers BRPM and DRPM the increased pollution *reduces* birth rate to reduce population and *increases* death rate to *reduce* population. At the same time, rising pollution ratio POLR *reduces* the food-from-pollution multiplier FPM, reduces the food ratio FR, and through multiplier BRFM reduces birth rate BR and population. Likewise through multiplier DRFM, the falling food ratio *increases* death rate DR to *reduce* population. The loops of Figure 2-7, wherein pollution stabilizes population, have probably not had a major impact in the past. But reports on shortened life span from continuous exposure to pollution and deaths due to sudden short-term rises in pollution both suggest that these loops are beginning to be active. In the future they may dominate if population and capital investment continue to increase.

2.8 Population Controlled by Natural Resources

Figure 2-8 shows loops connecting population and natural resources. In these loops rising population uses natural resources until the falling material standard of

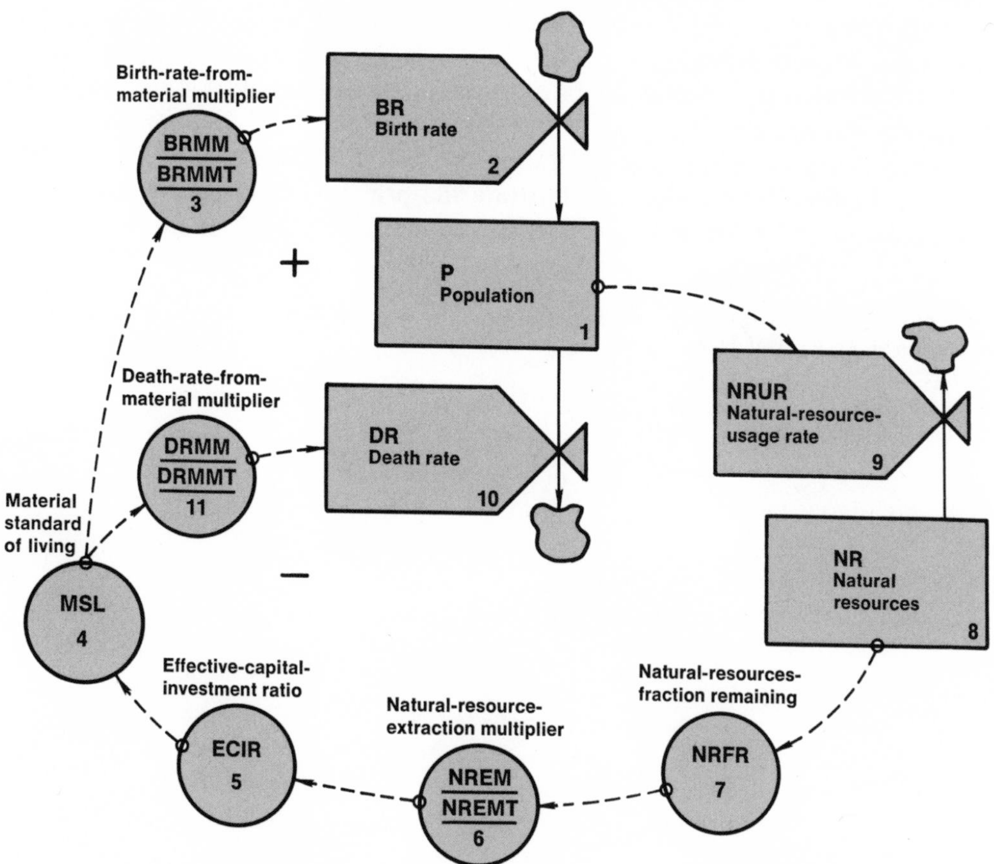

Figure 2-8 Negative loops that adjust population to the largest number that the natural resources will support.

living pulls population down again. If population P increases, the natural-resource-usage rate NRUR increases and speeds the *depletion* of natural resources NR to lower the natural-resource fraction remaining NRFR and lower the natural-resource-extraction multiplier NREM. This in turn reduces the effective-capital-investment ratio ECIR and the material standard of living MSL. The falling material standard of living MSL *increases* the birth-rate-from-material multiplier BRMM and increases birth rate BR; but this increase is offset by an increase in the death-rate-from-material multiplier DRMM to *increase* death rate DR and *reduce* population P. Here one of the branches is a positive loop, and the other branch is a negative loop.

The positive-feedback loop in Figure 2-3 and the negative-feedback structure in Figure 2-8 share a common point at the effective-capital-investment ratio ECIR. Through this common point, the subsystem of Figure 2-8 is able to depress and eliminate the growth capability of the positive loop in Figure 2-3. Depletion of natural resources NR in Figure 2-8 causes the effective-capital-investment ratio ECIR to decline. In Figure 2-3, the decline in effective-capital-investment ratio reduces the vigor of the capital-produces-capital process until capital generation is no longer able to exceed capital discard (involving the negative loop of capital investment CI and capital-investment discard CID). It is at common tie points such as ECIR that the negative loops of a system are ultimately able to overpower the growth mechanisms.*

Other feedback loops can be traced through the structure of Figure 2-1. However, Figures 2-2 through 2-8 illustrate the principle dynamic structures that account for the behavior that will be examined in Chapters 4, 5, and 6.

*This is also illustrated in the interacting positive and negative loops in Reference 4, and in the suppression of urban growth by land occupancy as in Reference 5.

3 A World Model—Structure and Assumptions

Suggestion to the Reader: This chapter is somewhat more technical than the others. Yet each person should read enough to satisfy himself about the assumptions from which follow the consequences in Chapters 4, 5, and 6. The nature of this world model is given here in two equivalent forms—text and equations. Those readers who are not familiar with algebraic notation may wish to ignore the equations that are placed at the end of each subsection. Those readers who are conversant with equation terminology will find the equation form more precise than the text. The latter readers, if not familiar with the form of equations used in the DYNAMO compiler, should read Appendix A before continuing.

This chapter discusses each assumption incorporated in the world model adduced in Figure 2-1. Each symbol represents a concept or relationship that might be found in a mental model of the corresponding part of the world system. The formal model depicted by Figure 2-1 constitutes a theory about the structure of the world system. By the nature of its construction the model asserts that the relationships chosen for inclusion are important, that the omitted relationships are less important, and the "real-world" interactions can be represented usefully as described in the details of the model.

A computer model, because it must be stated explicitly, makes a theory unambiguous. The assumptions within the theory become visible. The assumptions can then be criticized. They can be compared with the assumptions in alternative proposed theories. Data and observations can be used to improve the assumptions.

A theory expressed as a computer model can be checked and verified in more ways than a verbal theory. Because the component assumptions are stated more clearly, they can be compared more easily with all available information. Because the dynamic consequences of the theory can be determined by computer simulation, the model system can be compared with behavior of the actual system.

Sections of this chapter are numbered to correspond to the symbols in Figure

2-1.* The section number, not including the chapter number, also corresponds to the equation numbers in the model.

The general description of the system has been given in Chapter 2. The detailed description follows. The reader should examine the assumptions and relationships for plausibility. If he were to engage in extending and refining the model, he would want to test his alternate hypotheses by altering the assumptions given here to determine which changes in assumptions result in significant changes in system behavior. We are interested in the possible modes of behavior of the world system. Before one is justified in devoting large amounts of time to individual assumptions, he should see something of the total system behavior. Also, after a system model is operating, it is possible to examine sensitivity of the system to the various assumptions and to identify which are most important and need to be refined. One makes most rapid progress by following an iterative procedure in which he quickly comes to an approximate model, then examines behavior of the system that has been described, and finally returns to improve the assumptions and the interpretations. This book is the first of such iterations; it is intended as much to present methodology as to yield conclusions. A second iteration involving a major review and improvement is in progress at the time of writing as described in the Preface. Other reexaminations and extensions can be expected to follow as interest continues to grow in man's place in the world ecology.

In this model, conditions in the year 1970 are taken as the point of reference for defining constants and variables. That is, world conditions are described relative to 1970 conditions.

3.1 Population P

Population in Figure 2-1 is a system "level" variable. A system level represents the process of accumulation. Mathematically speaking, the process is one of integration. Population at any point in time is calculated as the population at the preceding point in time, plus the people who have been added by the birth rate in the intervening interval, minus the people removed by the death rate. A level equation is a straightforward accounting procedure for increasing and decreasing, in accordance with the rates of flow, one of the quantities that is accumulated in the system. If the level variables are given, the system rates can be computed from them. Therefore it is only necessary to know the values of level variables to start the system in operation. Levels provide the system "memory" or continuity that carries the past into the future. An initial value must be supplied for each level variable in the system. Initial values are here estimated for starting the world model in the year 1900. Population for 1900 will be set at 1.65 billion people (the American usage is one billion equal to 1,000,000,000).

*For the reader's convenience, a removable copy of Figure 2-1 is supplied inside the back cover of the book.

```
P.K=P.J+(DT)(BR.JK-DR.JK)                                  1, L
P=PI                                                       1.1, N
PI=1.65E9                                                  1.2, C
   P        - POPULATION (PEOPLE)
   BR       - BIRTH RATE (PEOPLE/YEAR)
   DR       - DEATH RATE (PEOPLE/YEAR)
   PI       - POPULATION, INITIAL (PEOPLE)
```

3.2 Birth Rate BR

The birth rate is part of the positive-feedback loop shown in Figure 2-2. Basic birth rate depends on population P and on a coefficient BRN. Birth rate normal BRN states the birth rate per year as a fraction of the population. Birth rate BR, as defined here, is the total rate at which people are being added to the population. It is measured in people per year. In demography, "birth rate" is more often defined as the rate per thousand of population, or the births as a percentage of the population, and is more comparable to the coefficient for birth rate normal BRN used here. The basic birth rate is then the population P multiplied by the birth rate normal BRN. BRN is measured in terms of people per year per person or as a fraction per year of the population that will be added by the birth rate.

But the actual birth rate depends on conditions in other parts of the world system outside the population sector. In particular, birth rate will depend on the condition of capital investment and natural resources as they manifest themselves in material standard of living, on crowding, on food availability, and on pollution. These effects from other parts of the system are introduced as "multipliers" that modify the basic birth rate. The multipliers vary from a "normal" value of 1. In other words, for a normal condition that is taken as the reference of comparison, the multiplier would not alter the basic birth rate. If the condition were more favorable than normal, the multiplier would have a value greater than 1. If the condition of a part of the system should be less favorable than normal, the corresponding multiplier would have a value less than 1.

The "normal" conditions for this model will be taken as the world conditions existing in 1970. That is, the multipliers will have values of 1 throughout the system when the system levels (population, capital, natural resources, capital in agriculture, and pollution) have their 1970 values.

The actual birth rate is then the basic birth rate as generated by the product of population P and birth rate normal BRN, multiplied by the four multipliers which are: birth-rate-from-material multiplier BRMM, birth-rate-from-crowding multiplier BRCM, birth-rate-from-food multiplier BRFM, and birth-rate-from-pollution multiplier BRPM.

Only the value of the coefficient BRN for birth rate normal remains to be discussed in connection with birth rate. Birth rate normal BRN in the model is not equivalent to the demographic "births per thousand" unless the birth-rate multipliers all have unity values. Generally speaking the multipliers will not be of unity value, and so the coefficient BRN does not give directly the births per thousand. However, if we assume that the multipliers have a unity value, as they do for 1970, we can estimate some reasonable values for BRN and the death rate normal DRN. Taking a world population of 1.6 billion in 1900 and a world population of 3.6 billion in 1970, the cumulative growth rate has averaged 1.2% per year. This is the difference between the birth rate and the death rate which we will here take as the difference between the coefficients BRN and DRN. A value of 0.04 for BRN and a value of 0.028 for DRN would satisfy this 1.2% difference and would be compatible with observed demographic rates for the first three-quarters of this century. The reciprocal of death rate normal DRN of 0.028 implies a life expectancy at birth of 36 years (including infant mortality).

The values chosen for coefficients such as BRN and DRN are not critical as long as they lie in a reasonable range. The powerful feedback loops described in Chapter 2 regulate the actual birth and death rates in response to the world conditions and will compensate, over a wide range, for changes in the values of the "normal" coefficients. This insensitivity, as to the values of BRN and DRN, will be demonstrated in Chapter 5.

```
BR.KL=(P.K)(CLIP(BRN,BRN1,SWT1,TIME.K))(BRFM.K)        2, R
  (BRMM.K)(BRCM.K)(BRPM.K)
BRN=.04                                                2.2, C
BRN1=.04                                               2.3, C
SWT1=1970                                              2.4, C
    BR       - BIRTH RATE (PEOPLE/YEAR)
    P        - POPULATION (PEOPLE)
    CLIP     - LOGICAL FUNCTION USED AS A TIME SWITCH TO
                 CHANGE PARAMETER VALUE
    BRN      - BIRTH RATE NORMAL (FRACTION/YEAR)
    BRN1     - BIRTH RATE NORMAL NO. 1 (FRACTION/YEAR)
    SWT1     - SWITCH TIME NO. 1 FOR BRN (YEARS)
    TIME     - CALENDAR TIME (YEARS)
    BRFM     - BIRTH-RATE-FROM-FOOD MULTIPLIER (DIMENSIONLESS)
    BRMM     - BIRTH-RATE-FROM-MATERIAL MULTIPLIER
                 (DIMENSIONLESS)
    BRCM     - BIRTH-RATE-FROM-CROWDING MULTIPLIER
                 (DIMENSIONLESS)
    BRPM     - BIRTH-RATE-FROM-POLLUTION MULTIPLIER
                 (DIMENSIONLESS)
```

3.3 Birth-Rate-from-Material Multiplier BRMM

This multiplier modifies birth rate in response to changes in the material standard of living. The relationship chosen for the model appears in Figure 3-1. When the material standard of living MSL has a value of 1, it means that the world-wide aggregate material goods per capita are at the 1970 world average. This yields 1 as the value of BRMM and defines the meaning of the relationship. Picking the shape of the curve on either side of the unity point depends on how we believe material standard of living will cause birth rate to change. Material standard of living here includes the effect of medicine, public health, sanitation facilities, and all the results of industrialization. It appears that with rising material standard of living, birth rate and death rate both decline and partially compensate. This results in less change in the number of surviving children per family

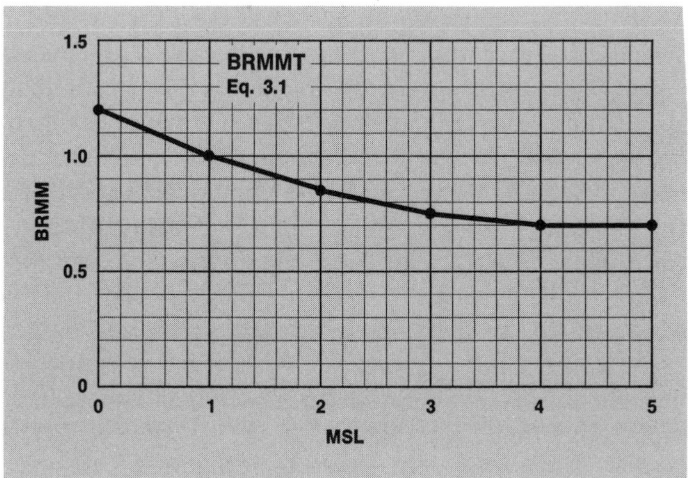

Figure 3-1 Birth-rate-from-material multiplier vs. material standard of living.

```
BRMM.K=TABHL(BRMMT,MSL.K,0,5,1)                          3, A
BRMMT=1.2/1/.85/.75/.7/.7                                3.1, T
   BRMM     - BIRTH-RATE-FROM-MATERIAL MULTIPLIER
                (DIMENSIONLESS)
   TABHL    - LOGICAL FUNCTION, TABLE LOOK UP AND
                INTERPOLATION
   BRMMT    - BIRTH-RATE-FROM-MATERIAL-MULTIPLIER TABLE
   MSL      - MATERIAL STANDARD OF LIVING (DIMENSIONLESS)
```

than the amount of change in the individual birth and death rates taken separately might imply. A relationship such as the one sketched in Figure 3-1 represents the effect of one system input only—the influence of material standard of living on the birth rate. The relationship is most easily interpreted by assuming that all other system conditions, except for material standard of living, remain fixed. The one single influence is illustrated. Of course, in the actual system, a changing birth rate would cause changes throughout the system. If food per capita, pollution, and crowding were not to change and if material standard of living alone were to vary, Figure 3-1 describes the effect on birth rate.

Relationships such as that depicted in Figure 3-1 must exist in real systems. To the extent that they are important in the controlling feedback loops, we must include them in models of real systems if those models are to show realistic behavior. But we must recognize that indisputable data on such a relationship will seldom be available. An estimate can only be based on fragments of information and on reasoning about likely behavior under extreme conditions. Consider a very low world-wide material standard of living, which corresponds to the left edge of Figure 3-1. How much would the average world birth rate rise were the world material standard of living to decline to near zero? For three-quarters of the world population this would represent very little change. Only for the one-quarter of the world population in the economically advanced countries would there be any substantial change. If we assume that the birth rate in three-quarters of the population is double the birth rate in the remaining quarter, doubling the rate in the one-quarter would increase the world total by somewhat less than 20 per cent. Figure 3-1 assumes a 20% increase for birth rate as the material standard of living drops toward zero. At the right-hand end of the figure, we expect the birth rate to decline, but the amount is not easy to estimate. High standard of living is usually associated with a higher adequacy of food, more crowding, and more pollution. These effects have probably not been reliably disentangled. It is doubtful that they could be separated on the basis of available data and data-analysis techniques. But because the kinds of conclusions that one is entitled to draw from dynamic models are usually not sensitive to most parameter values, we can proceed on the expectation that a reasonable estimate is sufficient. System sensitivity can be examined in future studies of the system. Figure 3-1 assumes birth rate to decline 30 per cent as the material standard of living rises by a factor of 5 from the 1970 world average.

3.4 Material Standard of Living MSL

The material standard of living is a nondimensional ratio that describes the extent to which effective capital investment per person is greater or less than the 1970 value. The value is defined as the effective-capital-investment ratio ECIR divided by the effective-capital-investment ratio normal ECIRN. A "capital unit" in the model system is defined as the capital investment available per person in 1970. Thus by definition, the value of ECIRN is 1 capital unit per person. The relationship has no numerical effect on the value from ECIR but maintains the intended dimensions of measurement.

```
MSL.K=ECIR.K/(ECIRN)                                      4, A
ECIRN=1                                                   4.1, C
   MSL     - MATERIAL STANDARD OF LIVING (DIMENSIONLESS)
   ECIR    - EFFECTIVE-CAPITAL-INVESTMENT RATIO (CAPITAL
               UNITS/PERSON)
   ECIRN   - EFFECTIVE-CAPITAL-INVESTMENT RATIO NORMAL
               (CAPITAL UNITS/PERSON)
```

3.5 Effective-Capital-Investment Ratio ECIR

Effective capital units per person are those capital units that contribute directly to improving the standard of living. The number of effective units per person is arrived at by applying to total capital units a discount that reflects any shortage in world-wide natural resources. A resource shortage means that capital plant becomes less effective as more and more of the capital investment must be devoted to mining more deeply, refining poorer ores, and using less efficient energy sources. To obtain ECIR, the capital-investment ratio CIR is first multiplied by the natural-resource-extraction multiplier NREM. The latter has a value of 1 at the original value of natural resources as they existed in 1900. But, for this study, the capital-investment ratio CIR is a measure of all capital regardless of how it is used. This model system separates capital into that used for agriculture and that used for all other purposes. Therefore, the fraction of capital not used in agriculture (1-CIAF) is multiplied at this point. CIAF is the variable fraction of capital that is allocated to agriculture. ECIR has been defined so that the "normal" value in 1970 should be 1. To make this true, the actual fraction of capital not used in agriculture (1-CIAF) must be divided by the "normal" fraction of capital not used in agriculture (1-CIAFN) where CIAFN is a constant that will be explained in Section 3.22.

To summarize, ECIR is the capital-investment ratio CIR, multiplied by the natural-resource-extraction multiplier NREM, multiplied by the variable fraction (1-CIAF) of capital not used in agriculture, divided by the constant (1-CIAFN) which is the "normal" fraction of capital not used in agriculture under 1970 conditions. The resulting ratio ECIR is, at any point in time, the ratio of effective capital units per person to the 1970 capital units per person.

```
ECIR.K=(CIR.K)(1-CIAF.K)(NREM.K)/(1-CIAFN)          5, A
   ECIR     - EFFECTIVE-CAPITAL-INVESTMENT RATIO (CAPITAL
                UNITS/PERSON)
   CIR      - CAPITAL-INVESTMENT RATIO (CAPITAL UNITS/PERSON)
   CIAF     - CAPITAL-INVESTMENT-IN-AGRICULTURE FRACTION
                (DIMENSIONLESS)
   NREM     - NATURAL-RESOURCE-EXTRACTION MULTIPLIER
                (DIMENSIONLESS)
   CIAFN    - CAPITAL-INVESTMENT-IN-AGRICULTURE FRACTION
                NORMAL (DIMENSIONLESS)
```

3.6 Natural-Resource-Extraction Multiplier NREM

A declining supply of natural resources is taken to reduce the efficiency of capital investment as shown in Figure 3-2. At the right-hand side, NREM has a value of 1 when all natural resources still remain as indicated by a value of 1 for the natural-resource fraction remaining NRFR. At the other extreme, if there are no natural resources, capital investment will be ineffective, and the multiplier is

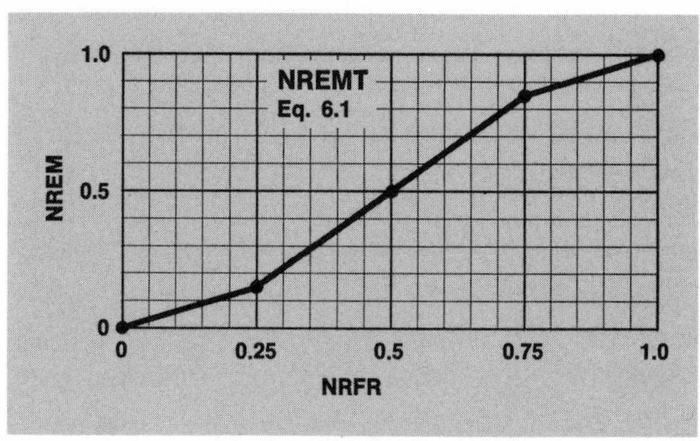

Figure Natural-resource-extraction multiplier vs. natural-resource fraction remaining.

```
NREM.K=TABLE(NREMT,NRFR.K,0,1,.25)                          6, A
NREMT=0/.15/.5/.85/1                                        6.1, T
   NREM     - NATURAL-RESOURCE-EXTRACTION MULTIPLIER
                (DIMENSIONLESS)
   TABLE    - LOGICAL FUNCTION, TABLE LOOK UP AND
                INTERPOLATION
   NREMT    - NATURAL-RESOURCE-EXTRACTION-MULTIPLIER TABLE
   NRFR     - NATURAL-RESOURCE FRACTION REMAINING
                (DIMENSIONLESS)
```

zero. The upper right end of the curve is nearly level because initial depletion of resources probably does not have much effect on availability of the remainder. Through the middle region, the curve is steep. At the left end, the curve again flattens and indicates the difficulty of extracting the last of any kind of natural resource as the supplies become more diffuse and the more difficult sources must be exploited.

3.7 Natural-Resource Fraction Remaining NRFR

The actual natural resources NR divided by the natural resources initial NRI gives the natural-resource fraction remaining NRFR.

```
NRFR.K=NR.K/NRI                                             7, A
   NRFR     - NATURAL-RESOURCE FRACTION REMAINING
                (DIMENSIONLESS)
   NR       - NATURAL RESOURCES (NATURAL RESOURCE UNITS)
   NRI      - NATURAL RESOURCES, INITIAL (NATURAL-RESOURCE
                UNITS)
```

3.8 Natural Resources NR

Natural resources are a system level. The only rate of flow is the outgoing usage rate. As defined here, natural resources include only those nonreplaceable materials in the earth. They do not include wood and any products that can be grown and replenished, for the latter are classed as part of the agricultural sector. The natural resources NR that still remain are computed at each time step by subtracting the usage rate NRUR multiplied by the time interval between computations.

An initial value is needed for each level variable. We define the natural-resource-usage rate NRUR in 1970 as being 1 natural resource unit per person. This is the world-wide average value. Furthermore, at the present rate of resource usage we will assume that the world's presently-existing natural resources would last for 250 years. Some clearly will last longer, some perhaps less. If in 1970 there are 3.6 billion people, then multiplying 3.6 billion people by 1 unit of natural resources per year per person and by 250 years gives 900 billion units of natural resources as the proper value for natural resources initial NRI. This figure comes from the *definition* of usage rate as one unit per year per person and the *assumption* of a 250-year remaining supply of natural resources.

```
NR.K=NR.J+(DT)(-NRUR.JK)                                   8, L
NR=NRI                                                     8.1, N
NRI=900E9                                                  8.2, C
   NR       - NATURAL RESOURCES (NATURAL RESOURCE UNITS)
   NRUR     - NATURAL-RESOURCE-USAGE RATE (NATURAL RESOURCE
                UNITS/YEAR)
   NRI      - NATURAL RESOURCES, INITIAL (NATURAL-RESOURCE
                UNITS)
```

3.9 Natural-Resource-Usage Rate NRUR

Natural-resource-usage rate NRUR is determined by the population P multiplied by the natural-resource usage normal NRUN and multiplied by the natural-resource-from-material multiplier NRMM. The natural-resource-from-material multiplier NRMM rises as the material standard of living increases—a rise necessary to represent the greater drain on natural resources that go with a higher standard of living. The natural-resource usage normal NRUN is defined as 1 natural resource unit per person per year, representing the 1970 world average usage rate.

```
NRUR.KL=(P.K)(CLIP(NRUN,NRUN1,SWT2,TIME.K))(NRMM.K) 9, R
NRUN=1                                              9.1, C
NRUN1=1                                             9.2, C
SWT2=1970                                           9.3, C
   NRUR     - NATURAL-RESOURCE-USAGE RATE (NATURAL RESOURCE
                UNITS/YEAR)
   P        - POPULATION (PEOPLE)
   CLIP     - LOGICAL FUNCTION USED AS A TIME SWITCH TO
                CHANGE PARAMETER VALUE
   NRUN     - NATURAL-RESOURCE USAGE NORMAL (NATURAL RESOURCE
                UNITS/PERSON/YEAR)
   NRUN1    - NATURAL-RESOURCE USAGE NORMAL NO. 1 (NATURAL
                RESOURCE UNITS/PERSON/YEAR)
   SWT2     - SWITCH TIME NO. 2 FOR NRUN (YEARS)
   TIME     - CALENDAR TIME (YEARS)
   NRMM     - NATURAL-RESOURCE-FROM-MATERIAL MULTIPLIER
                (DIMENSIONLESS)
```

3.10 Death Rate DR

Death rate has already been partially discussed in Section 3.2 in connection with birth rate. Basic death rate is population P multiplied by the death rate normal DRN. But the actual death rate, like the birth rate, depends on conditions in other parts of the world system. Food, crowding, material standard of living, and pollution are introduced through multipliers that have values of 1 for 1970 conditions and change as conditions change. The value of death rate normal DRN of 0.028 was discussed along with birth rate and is equivalent to an average life expectancy of 36 years. This may be low. Raising the figure, however, would require a compensating change in birth rate normal BRN to give the correct population growth rate between 1900 and 1970, and so the effect of any change would be slight.

```
DR.KL=(P.K)(CLIP(DRN,DRN1,SWT3,TIME.K))(DRMM.K)          10, R
  (DRPM.K)(DRFM.K)(DRCM.K)
DRN=.028                                                   10.2, C
DRN1=.028                                                  10.3, C
SWT3=1970                                                  10.4, C
   DR      - DEATH RATE (PEOPLE/YEAR)
   P       - POPULATION (PEOPLE)
   CLIP    - LOGICAL FUNCTION USED AS A TIME SWITCH TO
               CHANGE PARAMETER VALUE
   DRN     - DEATH RATE NORMAL (FRACTION/YEAR)
   DRN1    - DEATH RATE NORMAL NO. 1 (FRACTION/YEAR)
   SWT3    - SWITCH TIME NO. 3 FOR DRN (YEARS)
   TIME    - CALENDAR TIME (YEARS)
   DRMM    - DEATH-RATE-FROM-MATERIAL MULTIPLIER
               (DIMENSIONLESS)
   DRPM    - DEATH-RATE-FROM-POLLUTION MULTIPLIER
               (DIMENSIONLESS)
   DRFM    - DEATH-RATE-FROM-FOOD MULTIPLIER (DIMENSIONLESS)
   DRCM    - DEATH-RATE-FROM-CROWDING MULTIPLIER
               (DIMENSIONLESS)
```

3.11 Death-Rate-from-Material Multiplier DRMM

The material standard of living, as reflected in health services and housing as well as other consequences of technology, has a pronounced effect on mortality. Figure 3-3 shows the assumed effect. It suggests that a very high material standard of living could reduce the death rate by a factor of 2 but no more. At the left extreme of the diagram, if the material standard falls to zero, the death rate is shown as rising by a factor of 3. It is possible that further examination will show that this relationship should be less influential—that is, the curve should rise less at the left and fall less at the right. As with the other multipliers, the 1-1 point (where the multiplier value is 1 at a material standard of living of 1) is taken as the definition of 1970 conditions.

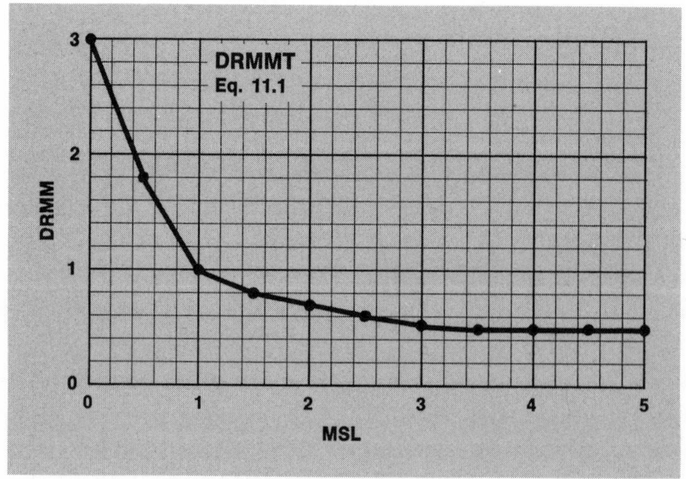

Figure 3-3 Death-rate-from-material multiplier vs. material standard of living.

```
DRMM.K=TABHL(DRMMT,MSL.K,0,5,.5)                    11, A
DRMMT=3/1.8/1/.8/.7/.6/.53/.5/.5/.5/.5              11.1, T
   DRMM    - DEATH-RATE-FROM-MATERIAL MULTIPLIER
               (DIMENSIONLESS)
   TABHL   - LOGICAL FUNCTION, TABLE LOOK UP AND
               INTERPOLATION
   DRMMT   - DEATH-RATE-FROM-MATERIAL-MULTIPLIER TABLE
   MSL     - MATERIAL STANDARD OF LIVING (DIMENSIONLESS)
```

3.12 Death-Rate-from-Pollution Multiplier DRPM

Pollution seems not to have been a major influence on death rate in the past. However, the increase in death rate that has occasionally occurred from sudden increases in pollution concentration, and the suspected reduction in average life span that is reported from living in high-pollution areas both suggest that we are at a point where continued rise in pollution will have progressively greater effect. Only the roughest of estimates are possible, for little dependable information exists. Figure 3-4 shows the assumption taken here for the way death rate depends on pollution ratio POLR. Pollution ratio is the ratio of world pollution level to the value of the world average in 1970. In the figure, a value of 60 for POLR means 60 times as much pollution in the world environment as in 1970. It is here assumed that the death rate would be doubled if pollution rose to 20 times today's value and that the death rate would rise by nearly a factor of 10 if

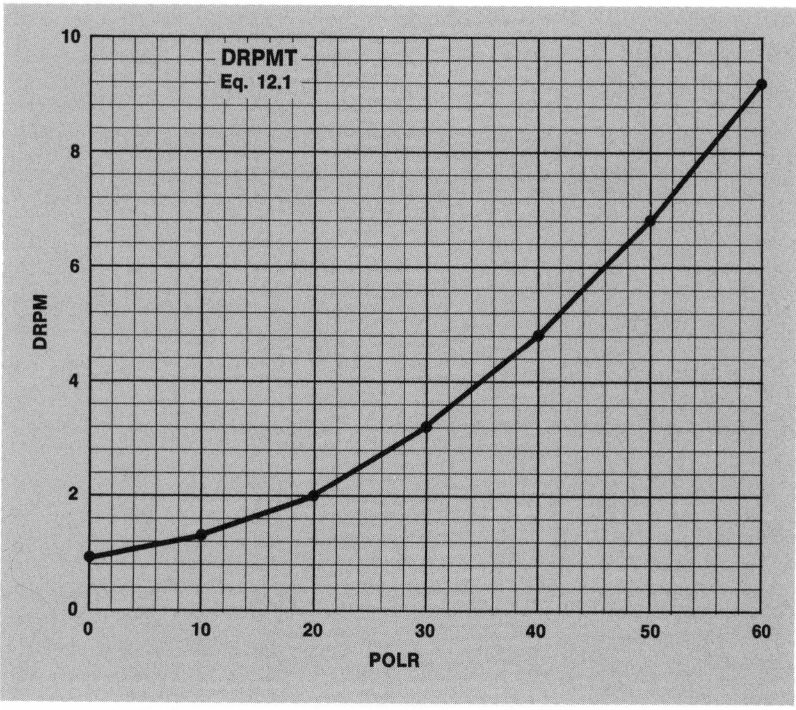

Figure 3-4 Death-rate-from-pollution multiplier vs. pollution ratio.

```
DRPM.K=TABLE(DRPMT,POLR.K,0,60,10)                    12, A
DRPMT=.92/1.3/2/3.2/4.8/6.8/9.2                       12.1, T
   DRPM     - DEATH-RATE-FROM-POLLUTION MULTIPLIER
                (DIMENSIONLESS)
   TABLE    - LOGICAL FUNCTION, TABLE LOOK UP AND
                INTERPOLATION
   DRPMT    - DEATH-RATE-FROM-POLLUTION-MULTIPLIER TABLE
   POLR     - POLLUTION RATIO (DIMENSIONLESS)
```

pollution rose by a factor of 60. Curves such as the one plotted in Figure 3-4 reflect long-term rather than instantaneous effects. Figure 2-1 contains no delays between POLR in Symbol 29 and the death rate in Symbol 10. If the progressive and delayed effects of a contaminated environment were to be included, they would take the form of delays with additional level equations in the information-feedback loops of the model. Additional system levels would introduce the possibility of other modes of population overshoot and collapse with population fluctuating to either side of the equilibrium values.

3.13 Death-Rate-from-Food Multiplier DRFM

Food can be a powerful regulator of population. If food per person falls toward zero, the death rate must of course rise steeply, becoming equivalent to an infinite death rate at a point where there is no food. Under the 1970 condition, which is here defined as a food ratio FR of 1, a significant fraction of the world population is undernourished, and some are actually on the verge of starvation. The effect is certainly to shorten average life span compared to that which would accompany a fully adequate food supply. Figure 3-5 at the right edge shows death

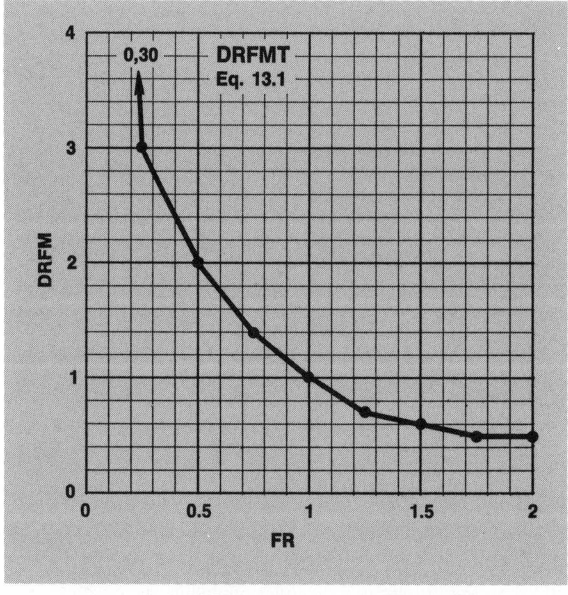

Figure 3-5 Death-rate-from-food multiplier vs. food ratio.

```
DRFM.K=TABHL(DRFMT,FR.K,0,2,.25)                              13, A
DRFMT=30/3/2/1.4/1/.7/.6/.5/.5                                13.1, T
   DRFM     - DEATH-RATE-FROM-FOOD MULTIPLIER (DIMENSIONLESS)
   TABHL    - LOGICAL FUNCTION, TABLE LOOK UP AND
                INTERPOLATION
   DRFMT    - DEATH-RATE-FROM-FOOD-MULTIPLIER TABLE
   FR       - FOOD RATIO (DIMENSIONLESS)
```

rate, on the average, falling by half if food were to increase by a factor of 2 per person on a world-wide basis. At the left edge of the diagram, death rate rises by a factor of 30 for no food, which is high enough to extinguish population within a year. A very steep rise to the left in the diagram is inescapable. To the right, one might argue that more food could not produce as much as a 50 per cent decline in death rate. The effect of a relationship like the one assumed in Figure 3-5 is to raise death rate when food per person falls and to reduce death rate when food per person rises. The result is to regulate population toward the maximum that food will support. At that maximum, keeping in mind the uneven distribution that has always prevailed and probably will continue to prevail, some fraction of the population will be at the starvation point. An increase in food raises the food per person for a short time until relaxation of the food pressures causes population to again rise to the limit set by the food supply.

3.14 Death-Rate-from-Crowding Multiplier DRCM

If no other influences were to intervene, sheer crowding would eventually limit population. At the ultimate limit, shortage of space to stand would stop the increase of population! But long before that ultimate is reached, other, more subtle effects of crowding can be expected to exert strong pressures. Crowding is here assumed to include psychological effects, social stresses that cause crime and international conflict, the pressures that can lead to atomic war, epidemics, and any effects from too many people that are not more appropriately defined into the other influences that are represented in the model.

Figure 3-6 shows the crowding effect that has been included. Crowding ratio CR is the ratio of people to the 1970 population. Up to the present level of world population, little effect on death rate has been assumed from crowding. However, as crowding rises toward 5 times the present population, the death rate is taken to rise ever more steeply and to reach 3 times the present rate, for a crowding ratio of 5.

Four multipliers have been incorporated in the death rate: DRMM, DRPM, DRFM, and DRCM. In a model formulation, the factors should be examined not only individually but also in combination. Would the effect of simultaneous extreme values of all multipliers still be reasonable? In Figures 3-3 through 3-6, the lowest values of the multipliers are 0.5, 0.92, 0.5, and 0.9. The product of these four is 0.2, which, if multiplied by the death rate normal DRN of 0.028 from Sections 3.2 and 3.10, gives a death rate per year of 0.0056 of the population. This is equivalent to an average lifetime of 178 years and is unreasonable by any historical standards. This reveals a weakness in the present formulation which could be easily corrected at the expense of additional complexity in the model. Whether or not it is significant depends on the values of the multipliers that are actually encountered in the use of the model. For the results presented in this book, an elaboration of the model structure does not seem justified.

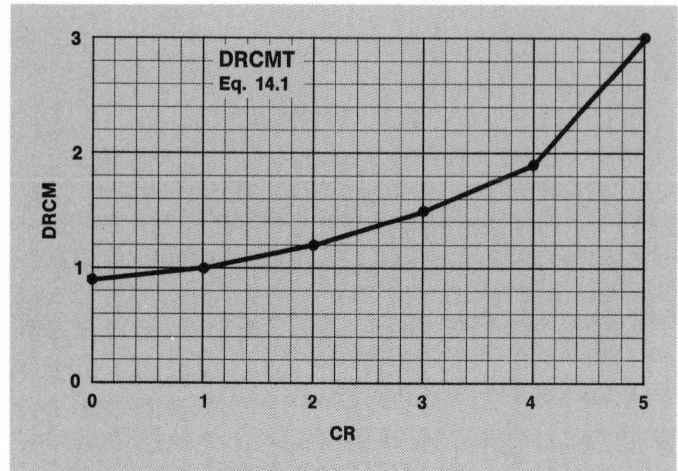

Figure 3-6 Death-rate-from-crowding multiplier vs. crowding ratio.

```
DRCM.K=TABLE(DRCMT,CR.K,0,5,1)                              14, A
DRCMT=.9/1/1.2/1.5/1.9/3                                    14.1, T
   DRCM     - DEATH-RATE-FROM-CROWDING MULTIPLIER
                (DIMENSIONLESS)
   TABLE    - LOGICAL FUNCTION, TABLE LOOK UP AND
                INTERPOLATION
   DRCMT    - DEATH-RATE-FROM-CROWDING-MULTIPLIER TABLE
   CR       - CROWDING RATIO (DIMENSIONLESS)
```

3.15 Crowding Ratio CR

The crowding ratio relates the population to the available land area. It is computed by dividing the population P by the land area LA and by the 1970 population density normal PDN in people per square kilometer for the world as a whole. The resulting ratio is in terms of 1970 crowding. A value of 1 is the degree of crowding in 1970. The value at any point in time is simply a multiple of the 1970 world population and is therefore also a multiple of the 1970 average population density. The land area LA is taken as 135 million square kilometers, and the 1970 average population density normal PDN is 26.5 people per square kilometer.

```
CR.K=(P.K)/(LA*PDN)                                         15, A
LA=135E6                                                    15.1, C
PDN=26.5                                                    15.2, C
```

```
CR      - CROWDING RATIO (DIMENSIONLESS)
P       - POPULATION (PEOPLE)
LA      - LAND AREA (SQUARE KILOMETERS)
PDN     - POPULATION DENSITY NORMAL (PEOPLE/SQUARE
            KILOMETER)
```

3.16 Birth-Rate-from-Crowding Multiplier BRCM

Figure 3-7 is the estimated effect of crowding on birth rate. The multiplier has a value of 1 for 1970 conditions. For less crowding, there is little increase in birth rate. For greater crowding, the influence becomes substantial and is taken here to cause almost a 50% decline in birth rate when crowding reaches 5 times that in 1970. The assumed effect is from psychological factors, fear, and the threat from world conditions. In estimating the value of this relationship, we must keep in mind that it is the average world-wide crowding that is indicated by the horizontal axis. The implications of high population density are quite different and more forbidding on a world-wide basis of extreme crowding than for small isolated centers of high population density that one can find in urban areas.

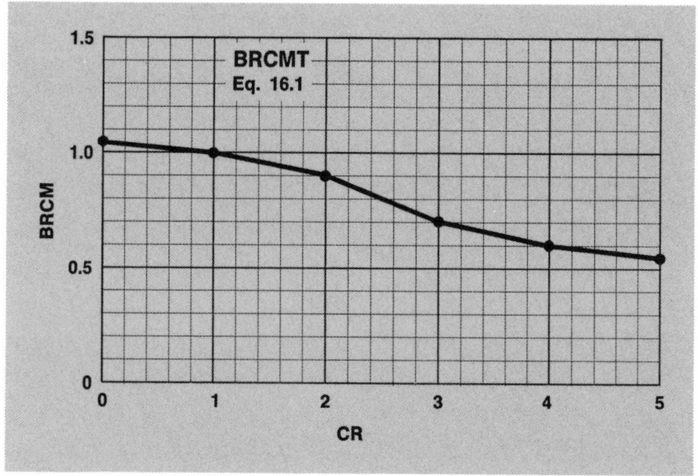

Figure 3-7 Birth-rate-from-crowding multiplier vs. crowding ratio.

```
BRCM.K=TABLE(BRCMT,CR.K,0,5,1)                       16, A
BRCMT=1.05/1/.9/.7/.6/.55                            16.1, T
   BRCM     - BIRTH-RATE-FROM-CROWDING MULTIPLIER
                (DIMENSIONLESS)
   TABLE    - LOGICAL FUNCTION, TABLE LOOK UP AND
                INTERPOLATION
   BRCMT    - BIRTH-RATE-FROM-CROWDING-MULTIPLIER TABLE
   CR       - CROWDING RATIO (DIMENSIONLESS)
```

3.17 Birth-Rate-from-Food Multiplier BRFM

The availability of food can be expected to have a substantial effect on birth rate, especially in the critical region where the population is undernourished. It appears that the world has normally existed in that sensitive region where food regulates birth and death rates so that population maintains its precarious existence at the maximum number of people that the available food can sustain. Figure 3-8 shows the relationship between birth rate and food ratio that has been used here. Food ratio FR is measured as a multiple of the per capita food in 1970. A ratio of 2 would represent twice the food per person that is found as a worldwide average in 1970. At zero food, life becomes impossible and, naturally, a zero birth rate is indicated. At the other extreme, an abundance of food is assumed to raise the birth rate by a factor of 2. At a high food ratio, there would be no threat of starvation, supplies would be ample, and health as attributable to food would be excellent.

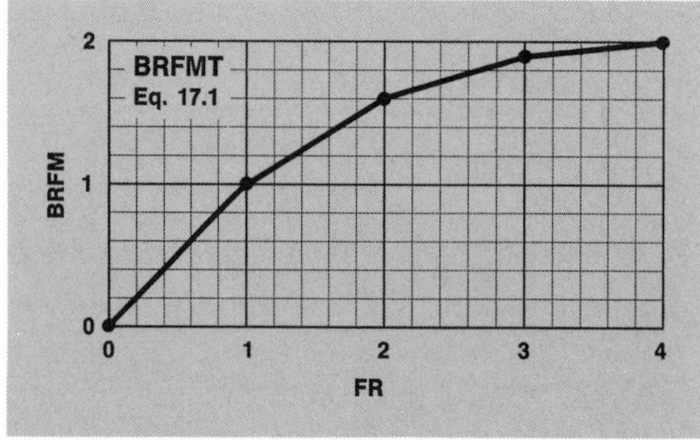

Figure 3-8 Birth-rate-from-food multiplier vs. food ratio.

```
BRFM.K=TABHL(BRFMT,FR.K,0,4,1)                          17, A
BRFMT=0/1/1.6/1.9/2                                     17.1, T
   BRFM     - BIRTH-RATE-FROM-FOOD MULTIPLIER (DIMENSIONLESS)
   TABHL    - LOGICAL FUNCTION, TABLE LOOK UP AND
                INTERPOLATION
   BRFMT    - BIRTH-RATE-FROM-FOOD-MULTIPLIER TABLE
   FR       - FOOD RATIO (DIMENSIONLESS)
```

3.18 Birth-Rate-from-Pollution Multiplier BRPM

At high levels, pollution is here assumed to exert a major effect on birth rate. It can act in several ways. The influence on health may be substantial, as has already been observed in bird and fish populations. In addition, very high levels of pollution can be expected to bring on great fears and social conflicts. In Figure 3-9, a pollution ratio POLR of 1 represents 1970 conditions. The graph extends to 60 times as much pollution in the world environment. Below the 1970 level of pollution, very little effect on birth rate is assumed. But, at extremely high pollution, the birth rate is assumed to drop to 10% of what it would otherwise be.

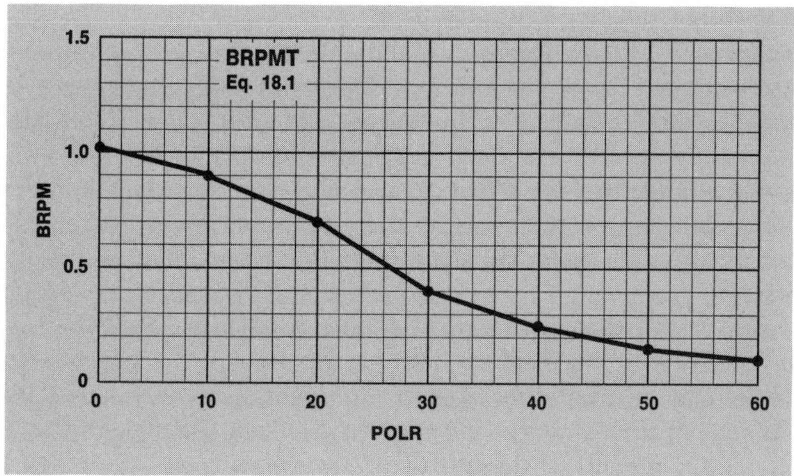

Figure 3-9 Birth-rate-from-pollution multiplier vs. pollution ratio.

```
BRPM.K=TABLE(BRPMT,POLR.K,0,60,10)                    18, A
BRPMT=1.02/.9/.7/.4/.25/.15/.1                        18.1, T
   BRPM     - BIRTH-RATE-FROM-POLLUTION MULTIPLIER
                (DIMENSIONLESS)
   TABLE    - LOGICAL FUNCTION, TABLE LOOK UP AND
                INTERPOLATION
   BRPMT    - BIRTH-RATE-FROM-POLLUTION-MULTIPLIER TABLE
   POLR     - POLLUTION RATIO (DIMENSIONLESS)
```

3.19 Food Ratio FR

The food ratio gives the food per capita in terms of the average for the world in 1970. It is a dimensionless ratio obtained by dividing the food potential from capital investment FPCI by the 1970 food normal FN and then multiplying by the influences of crowding and pollution and by a food coefficient FC. The two multipliers, FCM and FPM, and FPCI all have unity values under the normal conditions which are taken as those in 1970. More or less favorable conditions would correspondingly affect the available food per capita.

```
FR.K=(FPCI.K)(FCM.K)(FPM.K)(CLIP(FC,FC1,SWT7,          19, A
  TIME.K))/FN
FC=1                                                   19.1, C
FC1=1                                                  19.2, C
FN=1                                                   19.3, C
SWT7=1970                                              19.4, C
   FR       - FOOD RATIO (DIMENSIONLESS)
   FPCI     - FOOD POTENTIAL FROM CAPITAL INVESTMENT (FOOD
                UNITS/PERSON/YEAR)
   FCM      - FOOD-FROM-CROWDING MULTIPLIER (DIMENSIONLESS)
   FPM      - FOOD-FROM-POLLUTION MULTIPLIER (DIMENSIONLESS)
   CLIP     - LOGICAL FUNCTION USED AS A TIME SWITCH TO
                CHANGE PARAMETER VALUE
   FC       - FOOD COEFFICIENT (DIMENSIONLESS)
   FC1      - FOOD COEFFICIENT NO. 1 (DIMENSIONLESS)
   SWT7     - SWITCH TIME NO. 7 FOR FC (YEARS)
   TIME     - CALENDAR TIME (YEARS)
   FN       - FOOD NORMAL (FOOD UNITS/PERSON/YEAR)
```

3.20 Food-from-Crowding Multiplier FCM

Crowding will ultimately have a major influence on food production as already described in Figures 1-4 and 1-5. The more people, the more space occupied; and the more occupied space, the less agricultural land is left. Occupancy seems often to use the best land, and so the allotment of land of lower quality for food growing will increase the effect of crowding on food production. Population uses land for housing, working space, transportation, recreation, and pollution dissipation. Figure 3-10 shows the assumption that population has already pushed agriculture into marginal areas. At very low world population, we would expect people to cluster near the most productive agricultural areas. The figure represents the intrinsic nature of the land as well as reduction in the land remaining for agriculture. Effects of capital investment and pollution are introduced separately. At the left edge of the figure, the most productive land is assumed to be 2.4 times as effective as the present world average of agriculture land. At the right edge, a population of 5 times the present world population would force agriculture onto land of lower productivity as well as reducing the available food-growing land. The curve includes the effect of going to arid land where capital in the form of irrigation investments must be employed to compensate for the poorer natural conditions. Likewise, as the demand for food increases, artificial environments, greenhouses, ocean farming, and synthetic foods might be employed with a corresponding drain on capital efficiency.

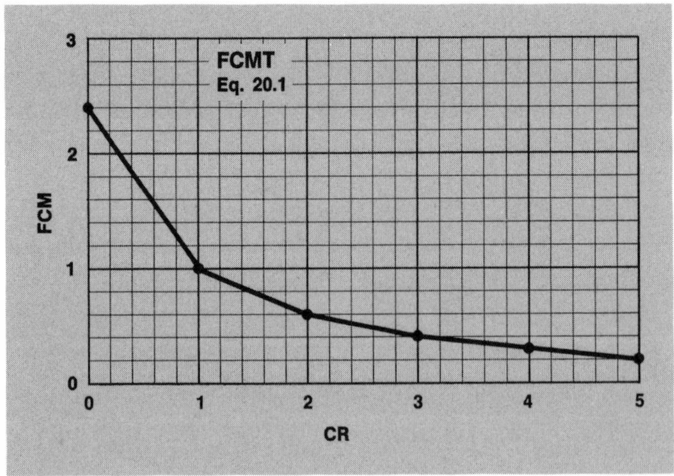

Figure 3-10 Food-from-crowding multiplier vs. crowding ratio.

```
FCM.K=TABLE(FCMT,CR.K,0,5,1)                                20, A
FCMT=2.4/1/.6/.4/.3/.2                                      20.1, T
   FCM       - FOOD-FROM-CROWDING MULTIPLIER (DIMENSIONLESS)
   TABLE     - LOGICAL FUNCTION, TABLE LOOK UP AND
                 INTERPOLATION
   FCMT      - FOOD-FROM-CROWDING-MULTIPLIER TABLE
   CR        - CROWDING RATIO (DIMENSIONLESS)
```

3.21 Food Potential from Capital Investment FPCI

The capital investment per capita in agriculture will be a major influence on the capability for producing food. Capital investment means here more than farm machinery. It includes fertilizer plants, irrigation systems, and the food processing and distribution systems. The capital-investment ratio in agriculture CIRA is defined to have a value of 1 for 1970 conditions. Figure 3-11 shows the assumed relationship for the influence of capital on food. With no capital investment, food production is still possible. It would imply a higher use of labor. Zero capital investment is here taken to decrease the food production of the world by 50%. At the high extreme for capital, the contribution of capital saturates, and more capital does little to increase food output.

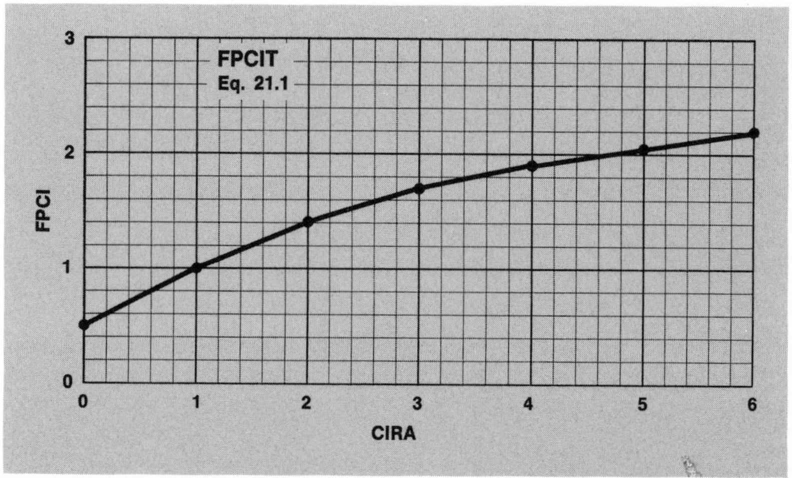

Figure 3-11 Food potential from capital investment vs. capital-investment ratio in agriculture.

```
FPCI.K=TABHL(FPCIT,CIRA.K,0,6,1)                         21, A
FPCIT=.5/1/1.4/1.7/1.9/2.05/2.2                          21.1, T
   FPCI     - FOOD POTENTIAL FROM CAPITAL INVESTMENT (FOOD
                 UNITS/PERSON/YEAR)
   TABHL    - LOGICAL FUNCTION, TABLE LOOK UP AND
                 INTERPOLATION
   FPCIT    - FOOD-POTENTIAL-FROM-CAPITAL-INVESTMENT TABLE
   CIRA     - CAPITAL-INVESTMENT RATIO IN AGRICULTURE
                 (CAPITAL UNITS/PERSON)
```

3.22 Capital-Investment Ratio in Agriculture CIRA

Food per capita is taken to depend on the agricultural capital investment per capita, called here the capital-investment ratio in agriculture CIRA. In keeping with other parts of the system description, we define the unity value as being equivalent to the condition in 1970. CIRA is computed as the total capital-investment ratio CIR, multiplied by the capital-investment-in-agriculture fraction

CIAF, and divided by the capital-investment-in-agriculture fraction normal CIAFN. The last term has an estimated value of 0.3 and restores the normal value of CIRA to 1 for the 1970 conditions. The result of the entire computation is to give a measure of the agricultural capital per capita to be used in determining the food ratio.

```
CIRA.K=(CIR.K)(CIAF.K)/CIAFN                                  22, A
CIAFN=.3                                                      22.1, C
   CIRA     - CAPITAL-INVESTMENT RATIO IN AGRICULTURE
                (CAPITAL UNITS/PERSON)
   CIR      - CAPITAL-INVESTMENT RATIO (CAPITAL UNITS/PERSON)
   CIAF     - CAPITAL-INVESTMENT-IN-AGRICULTURE FRACTION
                (DIMENSIONLESS)
   CIAFN    - CAPITAL-INVESTMENT-IN-AGRICULTURE FRACTION
                NORMAL (DIMENSIONLESS)
```

3.23 Capital-Investment Ratio CIR

The capital-investment ratio CIR gives the units of capital investment per person. Capital investment is measured in terms of 1970 per capita amount so the ratio has a value of 1 in the reference year. The ratio is computed as the capital investment CI divided by the population P.

```
CIR.K=CI.K/P.K                                                23, A
   CIR      - CAPITAL-INVESTMENT RATIO (CAPITAL UNITS/PERSON)
   CI       - CAPITAL INVESTMENT (CAPITAL UNITS)
   P        - POPULATION (PEOPLE)
```

3.24 Capital Investment CI

Capital investment is one of the system levels. It is created by accumulating the capital inflow from capital-investment generation CIG less the outflow to capital-investment discard CID. The net accumulation that has been generated and not yet discarded is, at any time, the current level of capital investment. An initial value is needed for capital investment in the year 1900. We assume here that the capital investment per capita in 1900 was 0.25 unit per person compared to the 1970 value of 1 unit per person. Because the initial value of population was nearly 1.6 billion, the initial value of capital investment was 1.6 billion times 0.25 or 0.4 billion.

```
CI.K=CI.J+(DT)(CIG.JK-CID.JK)                                 24, L
CI=CII                                                        24.1, N
CII=.4E9                                                      24.2, C
   CI       - CAPITAL INVESTMENT (CAPITAL UNITS)
   CIG      - CAPITAL-INVESTMENT GENERATION (CAPITAL UNITS/
                YEAR)
   CID      - CAPITAL-INVESTMENT DISCARD (CAPITAL UNITS/YEAR)
   CII      - CAPITAL INVESTMENT, INITIAL (CAPITAL UNITS)
```

3.25 Capital-Investment Generation CIG

The generation of capital investment is described as depending on population P, multiplied by capital-investment generation normal CIGN, and multiplied by the capital-investment multiplier CIM. Capital-investment generation CIG is measured in capital units per year. It depends on the population and on the average amount of capital each person accumulates per year. The coefficient CIGN, having a value of 0.05 unit per person per year, describes the normal accumulation rate for 1970 conditions. The multiplier CIM depends on the material standard of living and introduces a variable ability to accumulate capital depending on the capital already in existence. For 1970 conditions, CIM is defined to have a value of 1. If the material standard of living is lower than in 1970, the ability on a per capita basis to accumulate capital would be lower, implying that pressures would be higher for consuming currently all that is produced rather than saving to expand future production.

The value of CIGN of 0.05 is such that, for 1970 conditions, annual capital generation is equal to 0.05 of the existing capital investment. This is seen because

$$\begin{aligned} CIG &= (P)(CIGN)(CIM) \\ &= (P)(0.05)(1) \\ &= 0.05\ P \end{aligned}$$

Furthermore, in 1970 capital investment CI equals population P, both with values of 3.6 billion, because of the way a unit of capital investment has been defined as the 1970 per capita amount. With the 0.025 annual discard rate of capital estimated in Section 3.27 below, the net rate of capital accumulation for 1970 conditions would represent a current net increase that would cause capital investment to double in 40 years.

```
CIG.KL=(P.K)(CIM.K)(CLIP(CIGN,CIGN1,SWT4,TIME.K))    25, R
CIGN=.05                                              25.1, C
CIGN1=.05                                             25.2, C
SWT4=1970                                             25.3, C
   CIG      - CAPITAL-INVESTMENT GENERATION (CAPITAL UNITS/
                YEAR)
   P        - POPULATION (PEOPLE)
   CIM      - CAPITAL-INVESTMENT MULTIPLIER (DIMENSIONLESS)
   CLIP     - LOGICAL FUNCTION USED AS A TIME SWITCH TO
                CHANGE PARAMETER VALUE
   CIGN     - CAPITAL-INVESTMENT GENERATION NORMAL (CAPITAL
                UNITS/PERSON/YEAR)
   CIGN1    - CAPITAL-INVESTMENT GENERATION NORMAL NO. 1
                (CAPITAL UNITS/PERSON/YEAR)
   SWT4     - SWITCH TIME NO. 4 FOR CIGN (YEARS)
   TIME     - CALENDAR TIME (YEARS)
```

3.26 Capital-Investment Multiplier CIM

At extremely low levels of capital, the standard of living is low and the ability to accumulate capital is low. Under such conditions, almost all output must be used for immediate consumption. But as capital accumulates, production in excess of current need permits some of the output to be allocated to further increase in the capital pool. Figure 3-12 gives the capital-investment multiplier CIM in terms of the material standard of living MSL. Both MSL and CIM have values of 1 for 1970 conditions. At zero capital investment, which would mean a zero value for material standard of living, the ability to accumulate capital is taken as only 0.1 as great as for the average intensity of capital in 1970. The shape of the curve assumes that capital is not uniformly distributed in the hands of the population. As capital begins to accumulate, it is assumed to concentrate in the hands of a few people who can then rise above immediate consumption needs and thereby begin to accumulate more capital. Were the capital equally distributed at all times, the shape of the curve in Figure 3-12 might have a horizontal section at the left end before upward curvature begins. Such might keep the capital-regeneration process from starting. At the right side of the figure, the capital accumulation per person per year rises no further after capital accumulation reaches a point where more capital does not contribute to still greater human satisfaction. On the horizontal scale, a value of MSL of 5 would mean a world average of capital per person about equal to that of the United States in 1970. Even this non-rising rate of capital generation would cause capital to continue to accumulate to very high values before capital generation comes into equilibrium with the rate of capital-investment discard CID. One can argue that the curve in Figure 3-12 should rise to a peak and then decline at high material standard of living because the incentive for more capital accumulation would be satiated.

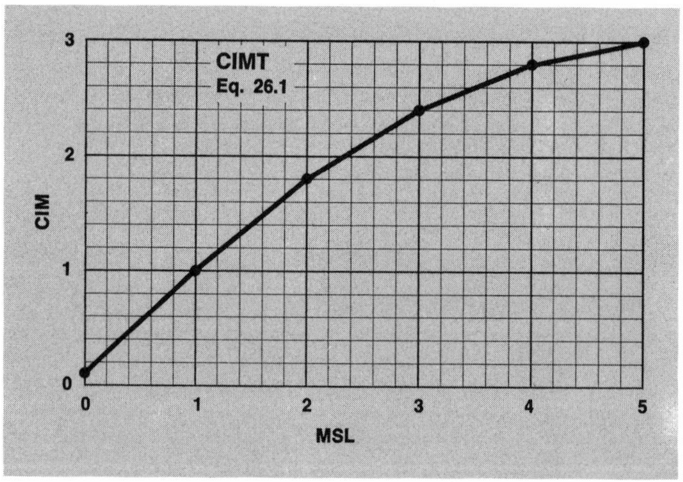

Figure 3-12 Capital-investment multiplier vs. material standard of living.

```
CIM.K=TABHL(CIMT,MSL.K,0,5,1)                        26, A
CIMT=.1/1/1.8/2.4/2.8/3                              26.1, T
   CIM     - CAPITAL-INVESTMENT MULTIPLIER (DIMENSIONLESS)
   TABHL   - LOGICAL FUNCTION, TABLE LOOK UP AND
               INTERPOLATION
   CIMT    - CAPITAL-INVESTMENT-MULTIPLIER TABLE
   MSL     - MATERIAL STANDARD OF LIVING (DIMENSIONLESS)
```

3.27 Capital-Investment Discard CID

The discard of capital investment is represented by a simple aging process. A fraction of the capital is discarded each year. This fraction is the capital-investment discard normal CIDN, having a value of 0.025. This fraction represents an average life which is the reciprocal, or 40 years. Capital includes buildings, roads, and factories. It also includes education and the results of scientific research, for the latter are not represented elsewhere in the model system and the investment in them decays at about the same rate as for physical capital.

```
CID.KL=(CI.K)(CLIP(CIDN,CIDN1,SWT5,TIME.K))            27, R
CIDN=.025                                              27.1, C
CIDN1=.025                                             27.2, C
SWT5=1970                                              27.3, C
   CID     - CAPITAL-INVESTMENT DISCARD (CAPITAL UNITS/YEAR)
   CI      - CAPITAL INVESTMENT (CAPITAL UNITS)
   CLIP    - LOGICAL FUNCTION USED AS A TIME SWITCH TO
               CHANGE PARAMETER VALUE
   CIDN    - CAPITAL-INVESTMENT DISCARD NORMAL (FRACTION/
               YEAR)
   CIDN1   - CAPITAL-INVESTMENT DISCARD NORMAL NO. 1
               (FRACTION/YEAR)
   SWT5    - SWITCH TIME NO. 5 FOR CIDN (YEARS)
   TIME    - CALENDAR TIME (YEARS)
```

3.28 Food-from-Pollution Multiplier FPM

Food production depends in part on the level of pollution. There is evidence that pollution is already beginning to affect farm crops in some locations and fish in the oceans. Figure 3-13 shows the assumed influence from pollution on food production. A pollution ratio POLR of 1 is defined as the pollution condition in 1970. The curve asserts that little effect from pollution has occurred up to the

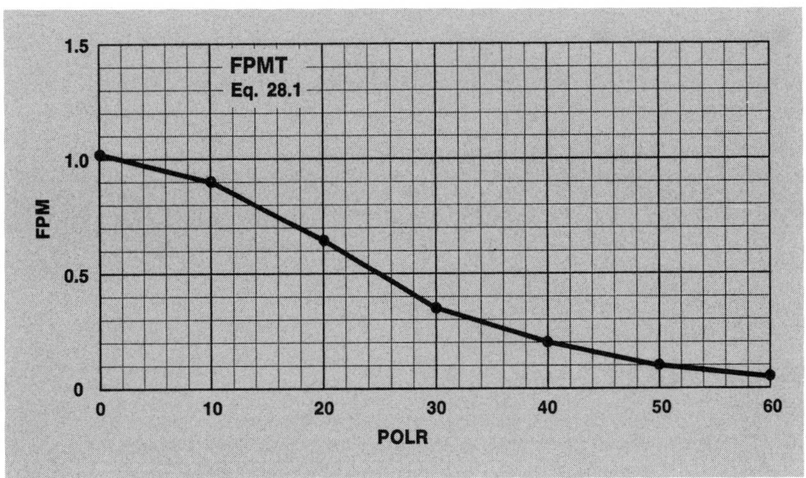

Figure 3-13 Food-from-pollution multiplier vs. pollution ratio.

```
FPM.K=TABLE(FPMT,POLR.K,0,60,10)                         28, A
FPMT=1.02/.9/.65/.35/.2/.1/.05                           28.1, T
   FPM      - FOOD-FROM-POLLUTION MULTIPLIER (DIMENSIONLESS)
   TABLE    - LOGICAL FUNCTION, TABLE LOOK UP AND
                 INTERPOLATION
   FPMT     - FOOD-FROM-POLLUTION-MULTIPLIER TABLE
   POLR     - POLLUTION RATIO (DIMENSIONLESS)
```

present levels but that the reduction in food productivity will become progressively greater as the pollution levels go to 60 times those in 1970. At 25 times the 1970 pollution, food productivity is estimated to fall to 50% of the pollution-free rate. For such high levels of environmental pollution, few facts are now available; yet it is probable that many of the weather, photosynthetic, and water-evaporation processes as we now know them would be unfavorably altered.

3.29 Pollution Ratio POLR

Pollution ratio is defined in relation to the 1970 level of pollution. It is computed by dividing the actual amount of pollution POL by the 1970 amount as given by the pollution standard POLS. The pollution standard POLS is defined as being one unit of pollution per person in 1970, and so is 3.6 billion pollution units.

```
POLR.K=POL.K/POLS                                        29, A
POLS=3.6E9                                               29.1, C
   POLR     - POLLUTION RATIO (DIMENSIONLESS)
   POL      - POLLUTION (POLLUTION UNITS)
   POLS     - POLLUTION STANDARD (POLLUTION UNITS)
```

3.30 Pollution POL

Pollution is one of the five system levels. It is a pool which pollution generation increases and which pollution absorption empties. Pollution POL represents the active pollution in the environment as it exists after generation and before dissipation into some harmless and inactive form. An initial value of pollution for the year 1900 must be specified. We here take one-eighth as much per capita as in 1970, giving (0.125)(1.6), or 0.2 billion pollution units.

```
POL.K=POL.J+(DT)(POLG.JK-POLA.JK)                        30, L
POL=POLI                                                 30.1, N
POLI=.2E9                                                30.2, C
   POL      - POLLUTION (POLLUTION UNITS)
   POLG     - POLLUTION GENERATION (POLLUTION UNITS/YEAR)
   POLA     - POLLUTION ABSORPTION (POLLUTION UNITS/YEAR)
   POLI     - POLLUTION, INITIAL (POLLUTION UNITS)
```

3.31 Pollution Generation POLG

Pollution generation POLG is taken as population P multiplied by the pollution normal POLN and by the pollution-from-capital multiplier POLCM. The multiplier POLCM represents the effect of capital investment per person on pollution generation. For conditions in the year 1970 it has a defined value of 1. The coefficient POLN should therefore equal the per capita rate of pollution generation in 1970. To arrive at a value of POLN, we must consider the size of the pollution reservoir POL in terms of its duration. How long does pollution remain in the level POL? Temporary pollutants such as smoke may be dissipated in a few days. Other pollutants such as insecticides, industrial wastes, and the detergent run-off may persist for years. We will use in Section 3.33 a "normal" pollution clean-up time-constant of 1 year as an average for 1970 conditions. So, with pollution being absorbed at a rate which would empty the level in one year, it must be generating at the same rate if the system is in equilibrium or at a somewhat greater rate if pollution is increasing. We here choose a generation rate that would create the present pollution in one year, assuming no absorption. This is a value of POLN of 1 pollution unit per person per year to produce 3.6 billion units in one year. (Pollution was defined for 1970 as being one pollution unit per person.)

```
POLG.KL=(P.K)(CLIP(POLN,POLN1,SWT6,TIME.K))            31, R
  (POLCM.K)
POLN=1                                                  31.1, C
POLN1=1                                                 31.2, C
SWT6=1970                                               31.3, C
   POLG     - POLLUTION GENERATION (POLLUTION UNITS/YEAR)
   P        - POPULATION (PEOPLE)
   CLIP     - LOGICAL FUNCTION USED AS A TIME SWITCH TO
                CHANGE PARAMETER VALUE
   POLN     - POLLUTION NORMAL (POLLUTION UNITS/PERSON/YEAR)
   POLN1    - POLLUTION NORMAL NO. 1 (POLLUTION UNITS/PERSON/
                YEAR)
   SWT6     - SWITCH TIME NO. 6 FOR POLN (YEARS)
   TIME     - CALENDAR TIME (YEARS)
   POLCM    - POLLUTION-FROM-CAPITAL MULTIPLIER
                (DIMENSIONLESS)
```

3.32 Pollution-from-Capital Multiplier POLCM

The amount of pollution generated per person is very much dependent on the capital investment per person. A person with no modern capital plant in his society generates very little lasting or harmful pollution. Pollution comes from power generation, raw-material conversion, chemical plants, waste disposal, and intensive agriculture. Figure 3-14 shows the way that rising capital-investment ratio CIR implies a rising rate of pollution generation per capita. Again, using 1970 as the point of reference, a CIR of 1 implies a POLCM of 1. The shape of the upper end of the curve might be debated. If the character of the capital plant were not to change as the amount of investment increases, the curve might continue its upward slope. On the other hand, if the high levels of capital investment imply capital devoted to pollution control, the pollution might no longer rise with increasing capital investment.

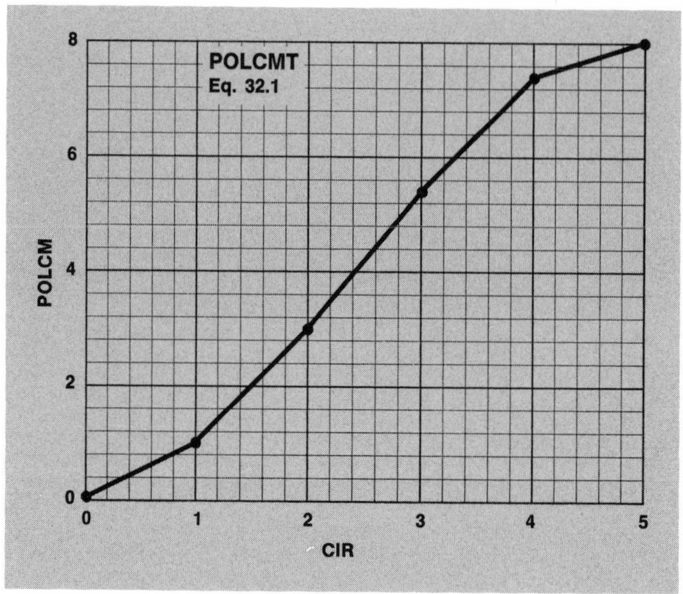

Figure 3-14 Pollution-from-capital multiplier vs. capital-investment ratio.

```
POLCM.K=TABHL(POLCMT,CIR.K,0,5,1)                              32, A
POLCMT=.05/1/3/5.4/7.4/8                                       32.1, T
   POLCM    - POLLUTION-FROM-CAPITAL MULTIPLIER
                (DIMENSIONLESS)
   TABHL    - LOGICAL FUNCTION, TABLE LOOK UP AND
                INTERPOLATION
   POLCMT   - POLLUTION-FROM-CAPITAL-MULTIPLIER TABLE
   CIR      - CAPITAL-INVESTMENT RATIO (CAPITAL UNITS/PERSON)
```

3.33 Pollution Absorption POLA

Pollution absorption depends on the existence of pollution to be absorbed. It also depends on the natural processes that determine the fraction of the pollution that can be absorbed in a specified time period. Pollution absorption POLA is determined by the amount of pollution POL divided by the pollution-absorption time POLAT. In simple decay processes, decay time is a constant. Such would be true for the spontaneous decay of radioactive materials for which one speaks of the half-life, which is the time required for half of any remaining material to disintegrate. But pollution absorption does not appear to be such a simple process. The time needed for a specified fraction of any existing pollution to disappear seems to depend on the amount of the pollution itself. The pollution-absorption time POLAT is therefore a variable rather than a constant. The structure of decay in the pollution sector therefore differs from that in the capital-investment sector where the capital-investment discard CID is controlled by the constant decay time given by capital-investment discard normal CIDN.

```
POLA.KL=POL.K/POLAT.K                                       33, R
   POLA     - POLLUTION ABSORPTION (POLLUTION UNITS/YEAR)
   POL      - POLLUTION (POLLUTION UNITS)
   POLAT    - POLLUTION-ABSORPTION TIME (YEARS)
```

3.34 Pollution-Absorption Time POLAT

Figure 3-15 shows how the pollution-absorption time is assumed to depend on the pollution ratio. The pollution-absorption time is the "time constant" of decay of pollution. It is the length of time needed for 63% of any existing pollution to disappear. It represents the same concept as the half-life of atomic decay which is the time for half of the material to disintegrate. A pollution ratio POLR of 1 represents the conditions exising in 1970. A value for POLAT of 1 year is taken for 1970. This means an assumption that under present conditions a year would be needed to dissipate about two-thirds of the existing pollution if all new pollution generation were to stop. For some of the polluting materials, that is too slow. On the other hand, one sees estimates that 90% of all DDT that has ever been manufactured is still in the environment. Certainly many kinds of pollution,

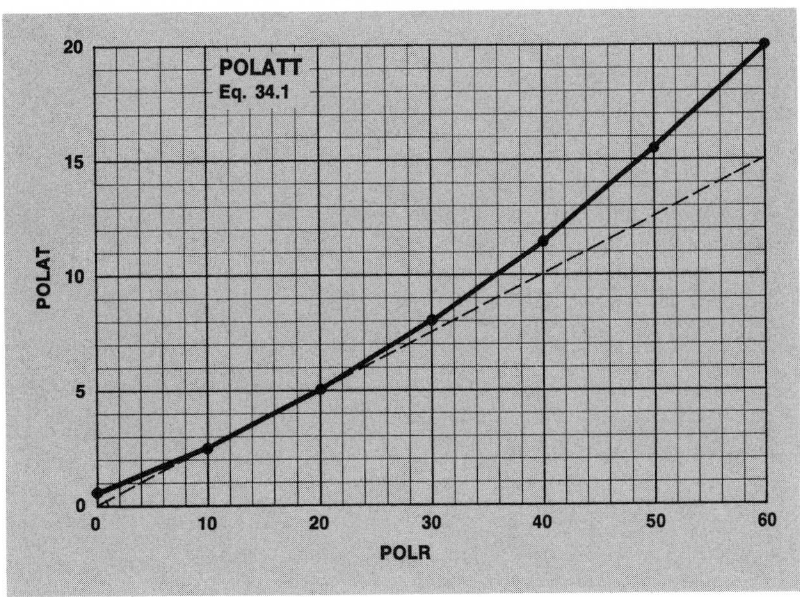

Figure 3-15 Pollution-absorption time vs. pollution ratio.

```
POLAT.K=TABLE(POLATT,POLR.K,0,60,10)                        34, A
POLATT=.6/2.5/5/8/11.5/15.5/20                              34.1, T
   POLAT    - POLLUTION-ABSORPTION TIME (YEARS)
   TABLE    - LOGICAL FUNCTION, TABLE LOOK UP AND
                INTERPOLATION
   POLATT   - POLLUTION-ABSORPTION-TIME TABLE
   POLR     - POLLUTION RATIO (DIMENSIONLESS)
```

probably including the more serious kinds, take longer than a year to disappear. A year is here used as an average. But as the amount of pollution increases, the pollution-absorption time is assumed to increase. This represents the poisoning and destroying of the pollution-cleanup mechanisms. Small amounts of pollution are dissipated quickly. But large amounts can have a cumulative effect by interfering with the natural processes of dissipation. Figure 3-15 suggests that the decay time for two-thirds of existing pollution rises to 5 years for pollution levels 20 times the 1970 values, to 10 years for a pollution increase of about 40 times, and to 20 years for 60 times the 1970 pollution. Such delay times are already observed. Many lakes may have become irreversible in their pollution or would recover only after times as long as shown in Figure 3-15. Estimates in the newspapers after the strike of sewerage-plant workers in England in 1970 gave estimates of 10 years for river life to recover to the condition it had before the excessive load of pollution. It is from this variable time constant that the pollution sector derives its virulent character. Above a certain level of pollution, even if the pollution generation is constant and not increasing, pollution absorption declines as pollution increases, and the processes become regenerative in a positive-feedback process. Pollution then increases rapidly until it becomes sufficiently high to reduce population and capital investment far enough that pollution generation falls back below the newly reduced rate of absorption.

3.35 Capital-Investment-in-Agriculture Fraction CIAF

Various choices could be made for handling the allocation of capital to different purposes. One could structure the model to generate capital investment separately for agriculture and for all other purposes. In this system the choice was to generate total capital and then to generate the fraction of that capital that is to be allocated to the agricultural sector. CIAF is generated as a gradual adjustment of the actual fraction of capital in agriculture as it moves toward the fraction that is called for by current conditions. The gradual adjustment introduces a delay that represents the time necessary for the changing mix of capital to be reallocated to the demands of the times. The adjustment time constant CIAFT is taken as 15 years, which is related to the life of capital and to the length of time needed to change substantially the mix of the capital in being. The actual capital-investment-in-agriculture fraction CIAF moves toward an "indicated" fraction that is derived from the condition of the food supply. The indicated fraction is computed from the capital fraction indicated by food ratio CFIFR multiplied by the capital-investment-from-quality ratio CIQR. The latter allows for a weighting of the quality-of-life factors between food and the material standard of living. The total effect of computing the capital-investment-in-agriculture fraction CIAF is to give food a priority over material goods so that the most pressing necessity of life gets preferred claim on the capital plant of the world.

CIAF is a system level and requires an initial condition. We start the system in 1900 with a value of 0.2 as the fraction of capital in agriculture.

```
CIAF.K=CIAF.J+(DT/CIAFT)(CFIFR.J*CIQR.J-CIAF.J)        35, L
CIAF=CIAFI                                             35.1, N
CIAFI=.2                                               35.2, C
CIAFT=15                                               35.3, C
   CIAF     - CAPITAL-INVESTMENT-IN-AGRICULTURE FRACTION
                (DIMENSIONLESS)
   CIAFT    - CAPITAL-INVESTMENT-IN-AGRICULTURE-FRACTION
                ADJUSTMENT TIME (YEARS)
   CFIFR    - CAPITAL FRACTION INDICATED BY FOOD RATIO
                (DIMENSIONLESS)
   CIQR     - CAPITAL-INVESTMENT-FROM-QUALITY RATIO
                (DIMENSIONLESS)
   CIAFI    - CAPITAL-INVESTMENT-IN-AGRICULTURE FRACTION,
                INITIAL (DIMENSIONLESS)
```

3.36 Capital Fraction Indicated by Food Ratio CFIFR

Figure 3-16 shows the fraction of capital which is taken as "proper" for various values of food ratio. As food declines, more and more of the total capital is indicated as desirable for food production. Reduced allocations are made as the food supply increases. An alternative model formulation would have been to cause a continuous flow of capital reallocation until the target of unity food ratio was reestablished. This latter might be better because the relationship in the figure does not insure that quality of life from food and from material standard of living are kept in reasonable balance with one another. The deficiency is partially corrected by the term described in Section 3.43. The result is to make the fraction of

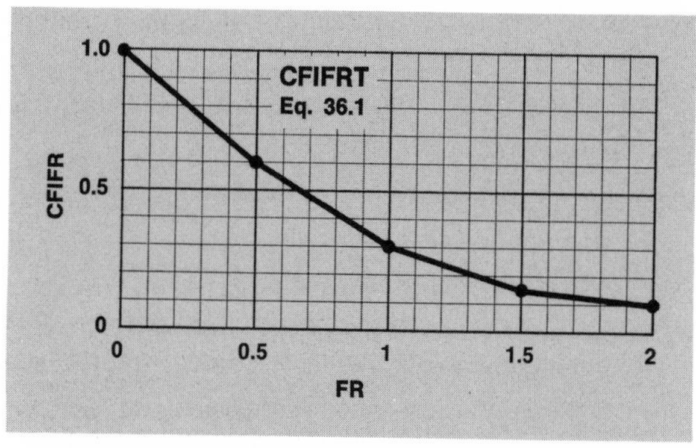

Figure 3-16 Capital fraction indicated by food ratio vs. food ratio.

```
CFIFR.K=TABHL(CFIFRT,FR.K,0,2,.5)                         36, A
CFIFRT=1/.6/.3/.15/.1                                     36.1, T
   CFIFR   - CAPITAL FRACTION INDICATED BY FOOD RATIO
               (DIMENSIONLESS)
   TABHL   - LOGICAL FUNCTION, TABLE LOOK UP AND
               INTERPOLATION
   CFIFRT  - CAPITAL-FRACTION-INDICATED-BY-FOOD-RATIO TABLE
   FR      - FOOD RATIO (DIMENSIONLESS)
```

capital allocated to food production dependent on the food supply and to temper this with an adjustment mechanism which operates according to whether food or material goods are the more critical at a particular time.

3.37 Quality of Life QL

Quality of life is used here as a measure of performance of the world system. It is computed as a quality-of-life standard QLS multiplied by four multipliers derived from material standard of living, crowding, food, and pollution. Quality-of-life standard QLS is the value of quality of life for 1970, which is defined as 1. The four component inputs to quality of life must be derived and combined in such a way that they properly reflect the urgency of the different components of quality of life. For example, a low food ratio is of more immediate and pressing concern than a low material standard of living or a high pollution ratio. Also, the adequacy levels of quality-of-life components are recognized. Above a sufficient amount of food, further increments of food rapidly lose capability to raise the quality of life. Likewise, below some acceptable level of pollution, further pollution reduction carries a low priority.

It is from the nonlinear character of quality-of-life factors that shifting emphasis comes. Throughout history, man has struggled first for food and second for material standard of living. Crowding has had a third-priority significance because crowding could often be relieved by invading thinly settled areas of the earth. Pollution was of least concern.

But priorities can reverse quickly. Pollution and crowding can rise to where they compete for attention even with the need for food. Furthermore, they both can reach a severity where they impinge on the primary needs for air, water, and food. These shifting priorities should be reflected in the composite quality of life QL which is generated from its components.

```
QL.K=(QLS)(QLM.K)(QLC.K)(QLF.K)(QLP.K)                    37, S
QLS=1                                                     37.1, C
   QL      - QUALITY OF LIFE (SATISFACTION UNITS)
   QLS     - QUALITY-OF-LIFE STANDARD (SATISFACTION UNITS)
   QLM     - QUALITY OF LIFE FROM MATERIAL (DIMENSIONLESS)
   QLC     - QUALITY OF LIFE FROM CROWDING (DIMENSIONLESS)
   QLF     - QUALITY OF LIFE FROM FOOD (DIMENSIONLESS)
   QLP     - QUALITY OF LIFE FROM POLLUTION (DIMENSIONLESS)
```

3.38 Quality of Life from Material QLM

Figure 3-17 shows the effect assumed here on quality of life from material standard of living. The multiplier is 1 at the 1970 material standard of living of 1. As MSL declines to zero, the quality of life is taken as falling to 0.2 of its former value if other conditions of the system remain the same. At the right side of the figure, an MSL of 5 would be equivalent to a world average about equal to that now in the United States. It is assumed here that such an improvement could be interpreted as increasing the average world quality of life by a factor of 3. There is no "right" vertical scale or steepness of slope to use in such a curve. The choice is arbitrary in picking the first relationship of the kind in Figure 3-17. As scales begin to be defined, other related concepts and interpretations must be consistent.

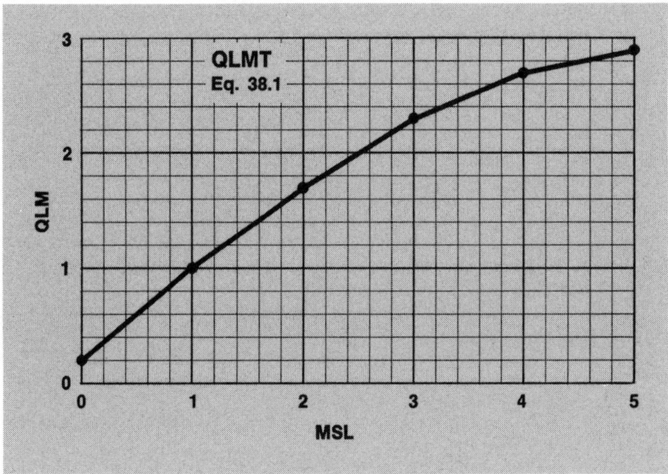

Figure 3-17 Quality of life from material vs. material standard of living.

```
QLM.K=TABHL(QLMT,MSL.K,0,5,1)                              38, A
QLMT=.2/1/1.7/2.3/2.7/2.9                                  38.1, T
    QLM      - QUALITY OF LIFE FROM MATERIAL (DIMENSIONLESS)
    TABHL    - LOGICAL FUNCTION, TABLE LOOK UP AND
                 INTERPOLATION
    QLMT     - QUALITY-OF-LIFE-FROM-MATERIAL TABLE
    MSL      - MATERIAL STANDARD OF LIVING (DIMENSIONLESS)
```

3.39 Quality of Life from Crowding QLC

Sufficient crowding will reduce the quality of life. The extent of the detrimental influence of crowding might be subject to disagreement. Figure 3-18 shows one assumption. The curve displays a high sensitivity to crowding in the range of CR equal to 1 at the 1970 point. The curve is shown as continuing to rise to the left as crowding (population) declines. Actually, at low enough population, the quality of life should probably no longer be considered to increase with increasing space per person. At the high-crowding extreme, the quality of life is taken as falling to 0.2 of its 1970 value. Crowding here implies all of the detrimental consequences of a high population density for the world—crime, psychological pressures, war and threat of war, lack of open space, and lack of privacy.

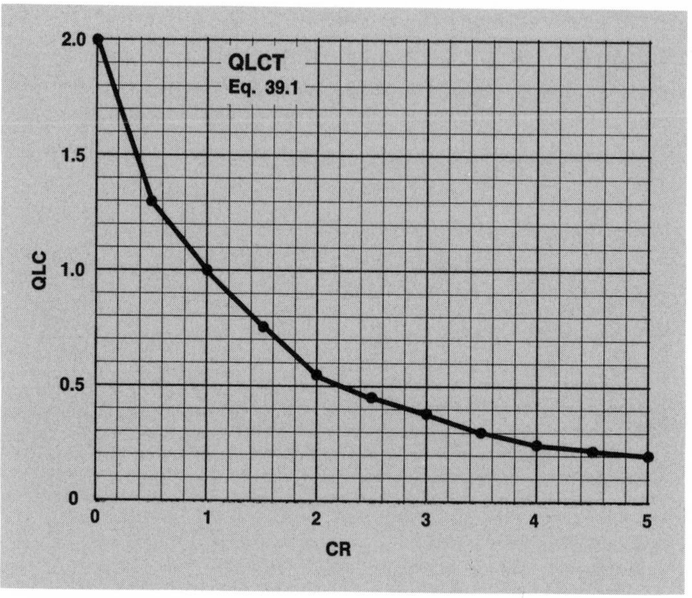

Figure 3-18 Quality of life from crowding vs. crowding ratio.

```
QLC.K=TABLE(QLCT,CR.K,0,5,.5)                              39, A
QLCT=2/1.3/1/.75/.55/.45/.38/.3/.25/.22/.2                 39.1, T
   QLC      - QUALITY OF LIFE FROM CROWDING (DIMENSIONLESS)
   TABLE    - LOGICAL FUNCTION, TABLE LOOK UP AND
                INTERPOLATION
   QLCT     - QUALITY-OF-LIFE-FROM-CROWDING TABLE
   CR       - CROWDING RATIO (DIMENSIONLESS)
```

3.40 Quality of Life from Food QLF

Food is the most powerful influence on quality of life. Figure 3-19 shows the quality-of-life multiplier as it depends on food. Perhaps the multiplier should approach zero even before the food ratio has reached zero. The quality of life QL is computed as the product of the separate components. This means that a zero component from food would reduce the entire quality of life value to zero, regardless of the values of other components of quality. As with the other components, a sufficiently high value of the food ratio might be reached where a further increase would not contribute to raising the quality of life.

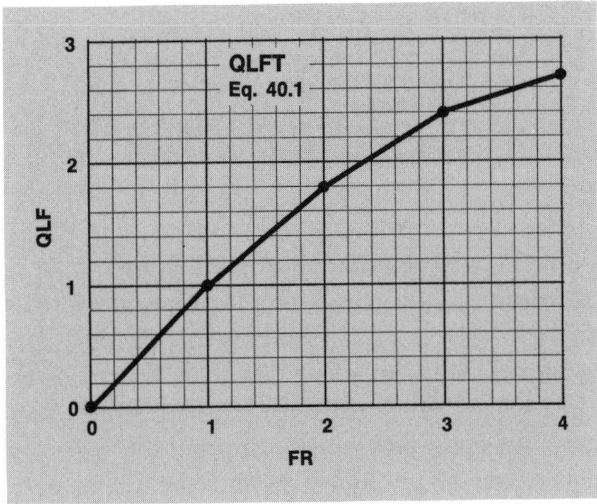

Figure 3-19 Quality of life from food vs. food ratio.

```
QLF.K=TABHL(QLFT,FR.K,0,4,1)                              40, A
QLFT=0/1/1.8/2.4/2.7                                      40.1, T
   QLF     - QUALITY OF LIFE FROM FOOD (DIMENSIONLESS)
   TABHL   - LOGICAL FUNCTION, TABLE LOOK UP AND
               INTERPOLATION
   QLFT    - QUALITY-OF-LIFE-FROM-FOOD TABLE
   FR      - FOOD RATIO (DIMENSIONLESS)
```

3.41 Quality of Life from Pollution QLP

We assume in Figure 3-20 that the quality of life for the average person in the world has suffered little from pollution up to the 1970 ratio POLR of 1. However, we are on the verge of progressively greater effect from pollution, and the curve shows an estimated steep drop in quality of life as pollution rises to 30 times the 1970 value.

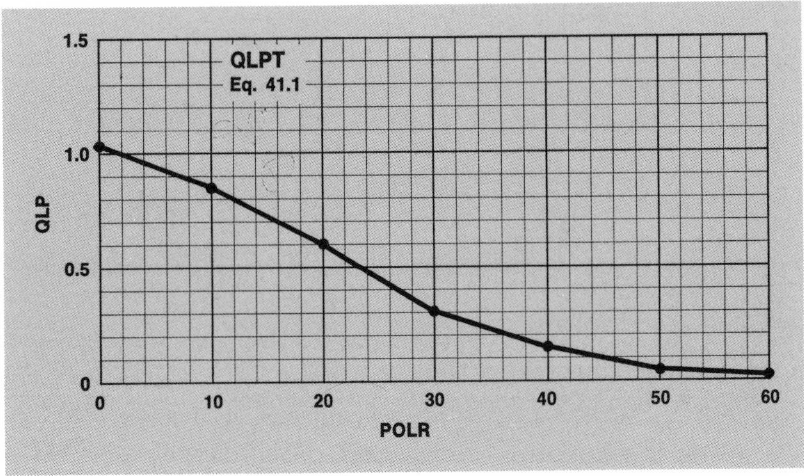

Figure 3-20 Quality of life from pollution vs. pollution ratio.

```
QLP.K=TABLE(QLPT,POLR.K,0,60,10)                           41, A
QLPT=1.04/.85/.6/.3/.15/.05/.02                            41.1, T
    QLP      - QUALITY OF LIFE FROM POLLUTION (DIMENSIONLESS)
    TABLE    - LOGICAL FUNCTION, TABLE LOOK UP AND
                  INTERPOLATION
    QLPT     - QUALITY-OF-LIFE-FROM-POLLUTION TABLE
    POLR     - POLLUTION RATIO (DIMENSIONLESS)
```

3.42 Natural-Resource-from-Material Multiplier NRMM

The usage rate of natural resources depends on population and on the material standard of living which reflects the amount of capital investment in the world. Figure 3-21 shows a relationship in which the use of natural resources rises with material standard of living, reaches saturation, and does not increase further. One might argue that the shape of this curve should not level out—the contention being that material standard of living *means* the use of natural resources. On the other hand, much of modern capital investment, which here is assumed to include research and the store of knowledge and education, does not deplete resources.

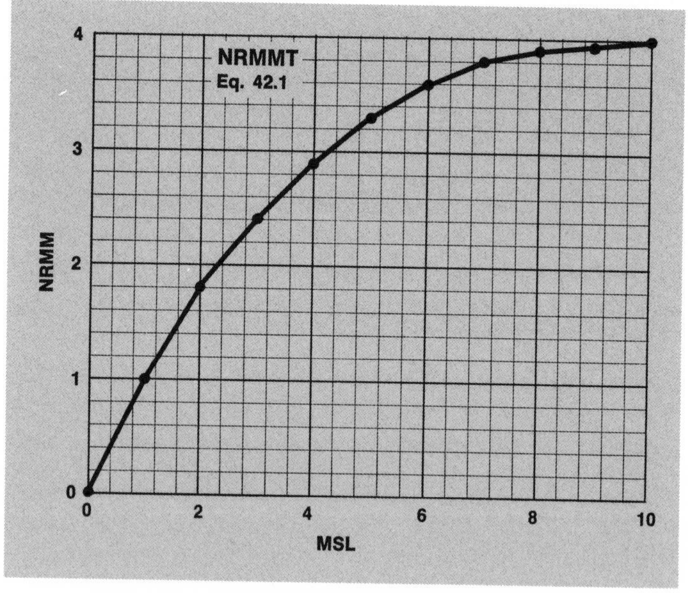

Figure 3-21 Natural-resource-from-material multiplier vs. material standard of living.

```
NRMM.K=TABHL(NRMMT,MSL.K,0,10,1)                           42, A
NRMMT=0/1/1.8/2.4/2.9/3.3/3.6/3.8/3.9/3.95/4               42.1, T
    NRMM     - NATURAL-RESOURCE-FROM-MATERIAL MULTIPLIER
                  (DIMENSIONLESS)
    TABHL    - LOGICAL FUNCTION, TABLE LOOK UP AND
                  INTERPOLATION
    NRMMT    - NATURAL-RESOURCE-FROM-MATERIAL-MULTIPLIER TABLE
    MSL      - MATERIAL STANDARD OF LIVING (DIMENSIONLESS)
```

3.43 Capital-Investment-from-Quality Ratio CIQR

The relationship in Figure 3-22 is introduced to keep the quality of life from material and the quality of life from food in a reasonable relationship to each other. The output CIQR from this figure enters the computation for the capital-investment-in-agriculture fraction CIAF in such a way that agriculture receives a higher capital allocation when the quality of life from material is higher than the quality of life from food. This prevents the system from allocating more and more resources to material standard of living unless the food ratio also rises correspondingly.

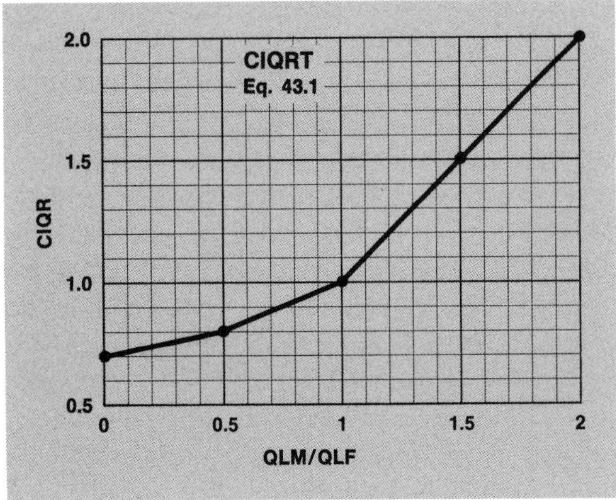

Figure 3-22 Capital-investment-from-quality ratio vs. ratio of quality of life from material to quality of life from food.

```
CIQR.K=TABHL(CIQRT,QLM.K/QLF.K,0,2,.5)                43, A
CIQRT=.7/.8/1/1.5/2                                   43.1, T
   CIQR    - CAPITAL-INVESTMENT-FROM-QUALITY RATIO
               (DIMENSIONLESS)
   TABHL   - LOGICAL FUNCTION, TABLE LOOK UP AND
               INTERPOLATION
   CIQRT   - CAPITAL-INVESTMENT-FROM-QUALITY-RATIO TABLE
   QLM     - QUALITY OF LIFE FROM MATERIAL (DIMENSIONLESS)
   QLF     - QUALITY OF LIFE FROM FOOD (DIMENSIONLESS)
```

4 Limits to Growth

Chapters 2 and 3 described assumptions about major world forces and their interrelationship in a dynamic model. Such a model constitutes a theory of behavior and interaction. Few people find the assumptions in Chapter 3 surprising. The assumptions seem to fall within the range of beliefs on which many of us are now acting. They appear close enough to the policies now governing our world system that it is worthwhile to examine how the assumed system behaves. On the basis of the explicit assumptions stated in Chapter 3, dynamic implications of the described system can be determined.*

Details of the system specified in the two preceding chapters give the rules of behavior that have been assumed. The rules describe how each part of the system is to operate in response to pressures and influences from other parts of the system. The rules allow a computer to play the roles of the various elements in the system. By allowing the elements of the model to interact, we can observe the dynamic nature of the system whose parts have been described.

To carry out the detailed simulation of the system we might choose any of many methods. A group of people could each act for a specific part of the system, following the rules of behavior that have been set down. Or, one could use an analog computer in which a separate piece of the machine is identified with each component of the real system. But less expensive and more reliable is the digital computer. The computer follows the instructions and traces system behavior step-by-step through time.

The system levels, shown as the five rectangles in Figure 2-1, determine the rates of flow. The rates of flow cause the system levels to change. The system can be "stepped" through time to unfold the behavior that is implicit in the original assumptions about the separate components.

*See References 2 and 3 for more information on modeling and computer simulation.

From the behavior of the system, doubts will arise that will call for a review of the original assumptions. From the process of working back and forth between assumptions about the parts and observed behavior of the whole, we improve our understanding of the structure and the dynamics of the system. This book is the result of several cycles of reexamination and revision by the author. Future improvement will come from those who can apply a different viewpoint and a more extensive background of knowledge. The behavior of the assumed world system will now be illustrated and discussed.

The model and its dynamic output together form a framework for organizing real-world information. Real-world information comes from two categories–observations about the behavior of parts of a system and observations about the whole system. We here mean "whole system" in the context of some particular mode of behavior. A whole system from one viewpoint is a part of a system from a different and more comprehensive viewpoint. A "viewpoint" is defined in terms of any designated set of interactions and time-sequences that we refer to as a mode of behavior.

The modes of behavior of interest in this book encompass the interactions that occur when exponential growth collides with a fixed environment. In other words, we here are examining the forces and interactions that can result from factors that are already known. We know much about the forces creating growth of populations and of industrialization. We also know much about physical limits of land area, the exhaustion of resources, and the overloading of capacity to dissipate pollution. What happens when growth approaches fixed limits and is forced to give way to some form of equilibrium? Are there choices before us that lead to alternative world futures?

Much concern is expressed about the importance of limiting population. We need have no fear that population will continue to rise forever. Exponential growth rates do not continue forever. Growth of population and industrialization will stop. If man does not take conscious action to limit population and capital investment, the forces inherent in the natural and social system will rise high enough to limit growth. The question is only a matter of when and how growth will cease, not whether it will cease.

The world model in this book contains four inherent forces capable of limiting population–depletion of natural resources, rise of pollution, increase in crowding, and decline of food. The following sections examine these four forces that stand in the path of continuing growth. Chapters 5 and 6 examine other kinds of world equilibrium that could be created by changes in social policies.

4.1 Reading the Computer Graphs

The figures in this chapter are drawn over graphical plots taken directly from the computer. The horizontal scale is in years.

In the line of type at the extreme left of the figure are the variables that are plotted and the symbol used for each. For example, POLR=2 means that the pollution ratio POLR appears on the graph as the symbol 2. The variables, like

POLR, are expressed in abbreviations used uniformly in Figure 2-1, in the sections of Chapter 3, and in the Appendix.

Vertical scales are printed at the left side of the graphs. In the extreme upper left, the scales are identified by the plotting symbols corresponding to the lines on the graph. For the numerical values on the scales, B indicates billions and M indicates millions.

Along the upper margin of the graph are letter groups associated with crossings of the lines on the graph; the first letter stands for all letters in the group.

Inserted at the top margin toward the left is an identification of the parameters and tables that were changed between the "present" computer run and the "original" model. The original model is the one with the values as given in Chapter 3 and the Appendix. In the listing of changed parameters, an A after a number indicates thousandths.

4.2 Natural-Resource Depletion

The system as described in Chapters 2 and 3 is discovered to be one in which growth is reversed by the pressures arising from declining natural resources. Figure 4-1 shows the behavior of the "original" world model as given by the equations in Chapter 3. The horizontal scale shows the time from year 1900 to 2100. Five variables of the system are plotted, giving four of the system levels and the quality of life. Population rises to a peak in the year 2020 and thereafter declines.

The decline in population is caused in this figure by falling natural resources. The falling natural resources lower the effectiveness of capital investment and lower the material standard of living enough to reduce population. At about the year 2000, natural resources are falling steeply. The slope of the curve is such that, if usage continued at the same rate, natural resources would disappear by the year 2150.

In Section 3.8 the supply of natural resources was assumed sufficient to last for 250 years at the 1970 rate of usage. But in Figure 4-1 the rate of usage (not plotted) rises another 50% between 1970 and 2000 because of the rising population and the increasing capital investment. Well before natural resources disappear, their shortage depresses the world system because of the natural-resource-extraction multiplier described in Section 3.6 that introduces the more difficult extraction task resulting from depleted and more diffuse stocks of resources. The effect of rising demand and falling supply is to create the dynamic consequences of shortage, not 250 years in the future, but only 30 to 50 years hence.

Discussions of the world system often rely on comparing present conditions with ultimate limits. By such comparison, present world demand usually seems well below the capacity of the environment. But two factors are usually overlooked. First, demand is rising with a doubling time of only a few decades. Second, the consequences of impending shortage begin to appear long before an ultimate limit is reached. As we see here, the effect of resource shortage appears far ahead of the time resources are exhausted and within only a quarter of the time that would be required for present rates to fully deplete present supply. The

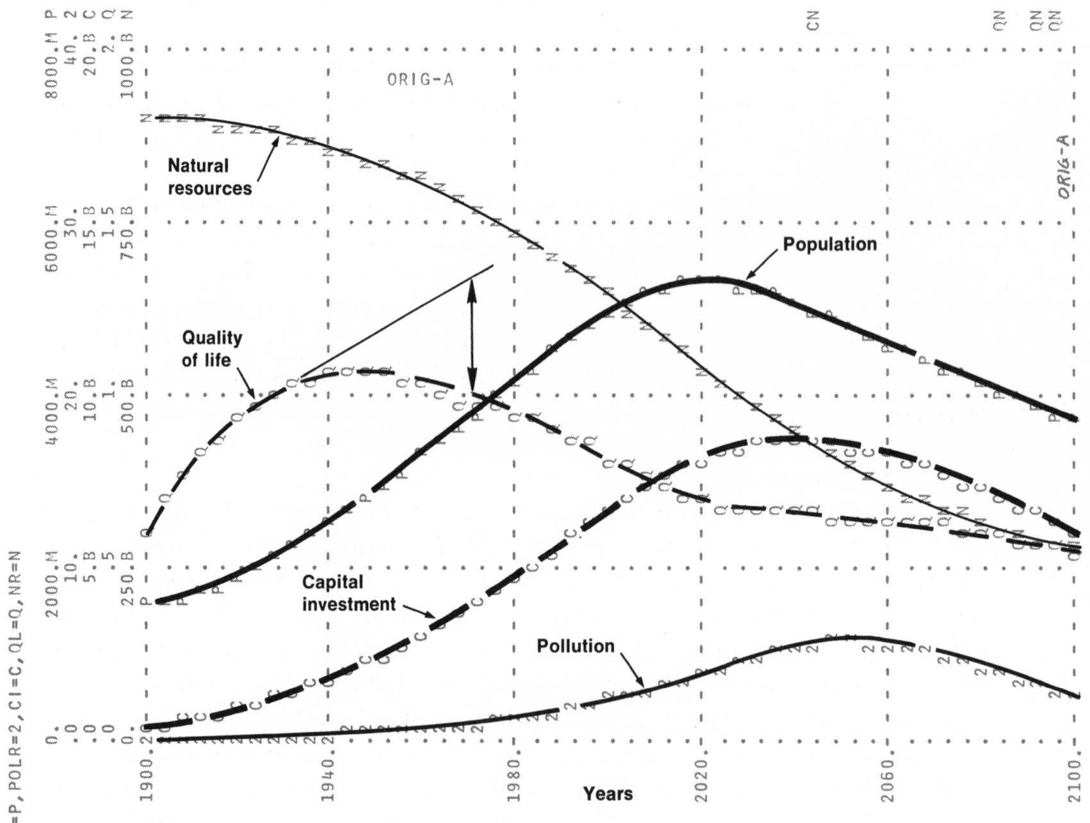

Figure 4-1 Basic behavior of the world model, showing the mode in which industrialization and population are suppressed by falling natural resources.

same accelerated pressures can be expected from food shortage, crowding, and pollution.

Many industrialized nations are now growing rapidly and placing ever greater demands on world resources. Many of those resources come from the presently underdeveloped countries. What will happen when the resource-supplying countries begin to withhold resources because they foresee the day when their own demand will require the available supplies? Pressures from impending shortages are already appearing. Will the developed nations stand by and let their economies decline while resources still exist in other parts of the world? Will a new era of international conflict grow out of pressures from resource shortage?

In Figure 4-1, pollution peaks in the year 2060 at some 6 times the level in 1970 but not high enough to cause the regenerative increase of pollution that will be seen in the next section.

Quality of life in Figure 4-1 peaks around the year 1960. It has declined very little by the year 1970 and is near its all-time high. Is this reasonable? How can

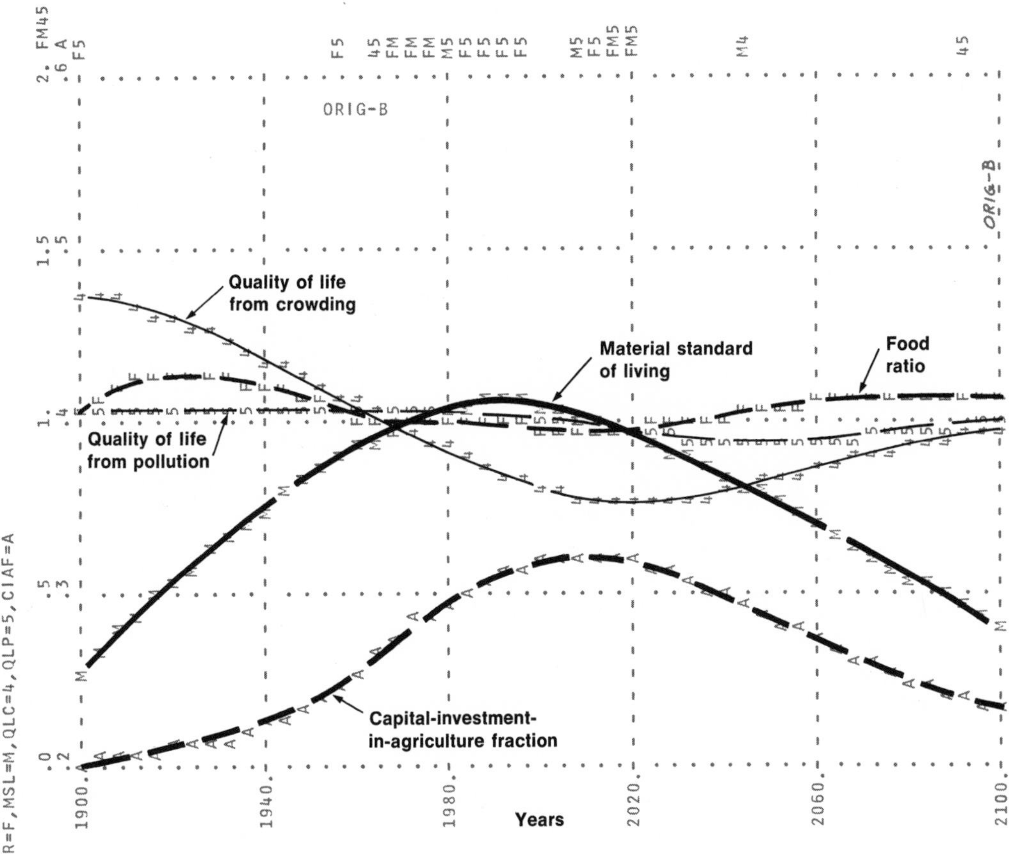

Figure 4-2 Original model as in Figure 4-1. Material standard of living reaches a maximum and then declines as natural resources are depleted.

one explain a historical maximum in quality of life at a time when the world shows rising social unrest? The two become consistent if we compare expectations with actuality. Figure 4-1 shows an extension beyond 1940 of the quality-of-life curve prior to that year. The extension continues to rise along the slope that had characterized the first part of the century. But the actual curve has fallen away from the extended slope. The gap between expectation and reality is shown by the arrow. A gap has opened between the extension of earlier trends and the actual quality-of-life curve, which has reached a peak and is starting to decline slightly. In fact, it is always at a peak or minimum of a varying quantity that the discrepancy between expectation and reality is greatest. The sense of disappointment is explained by Edward Banfield in arguing that although our cities are actually in better condition than ever before in history, yet they fall the furthest short of where we expect them to be (Reference 1).

Figure 4-2 shows four ratios related to quality of life for the same time interval and system conditions as in Figure 4-1. Also shown is the capital-invest-

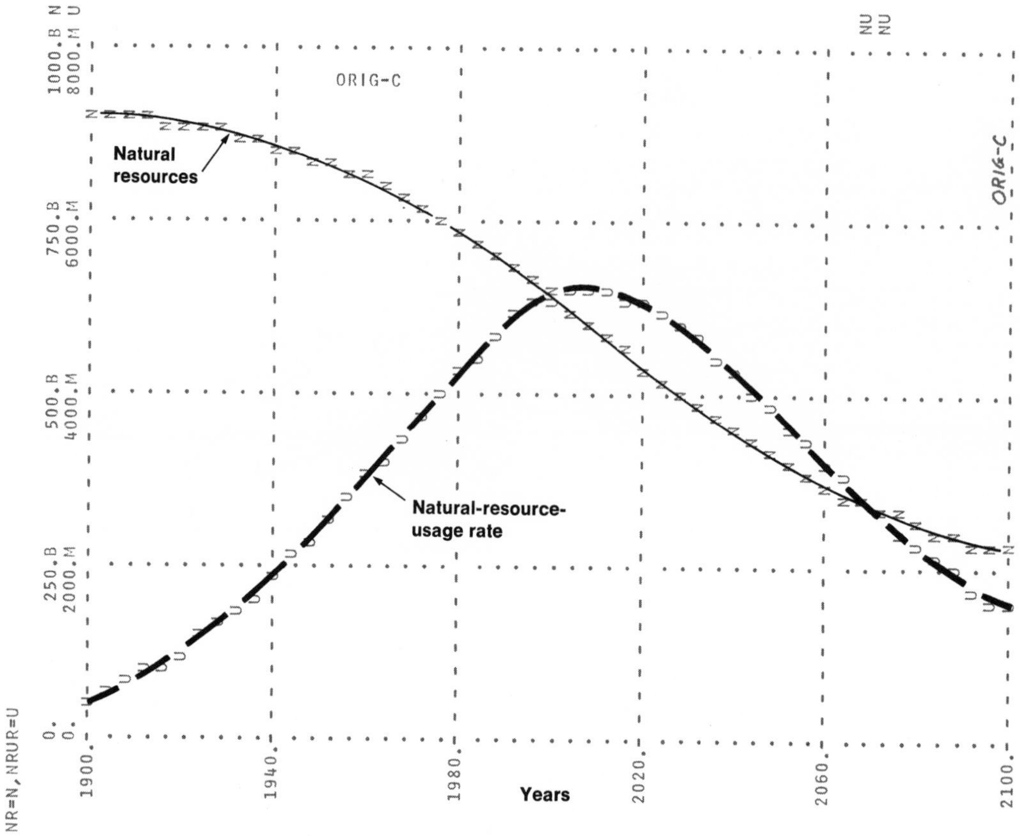

Figure 4-3 Original model as in Figure 4-1. Natural-resource-usage rate reaches a peak about year 2010 and declines as natural resources, population, and capital investment decline.

ment-in-agriculture fraction. Material standard of living reaches a peak at about year 2000 and then declines. At the peak, the capital investment per capita has risen, and the shortage of natural resources has not yet become severe enough to diminish the effectiveness of capital investment. Figure 3-17 in Section 3.38 shows the relationship between material standard of living and quality of life. In Figure 4-2 the capital-investment-in-agriculture fraction rises during the first hundred years from 0.2 to 0.32. This rise occurs for two reasons that can be seen in Figure 4-2. The material standard of living climbs so that there is less pressure to allocate capital for a higher standard of living. Also the food ratio is falling slightly, and the food ratio is a strong determinant of the allocation of capital to food growing. In the right half of the diagram, the falling material standard of living and the rising food ratio reverse the demand for capital in agriculture. Quality of life from crowding falls and then rises again as the population rises and then falls. Quality of life from pollution is inversely related to the pollution curve of Figure 4-1.

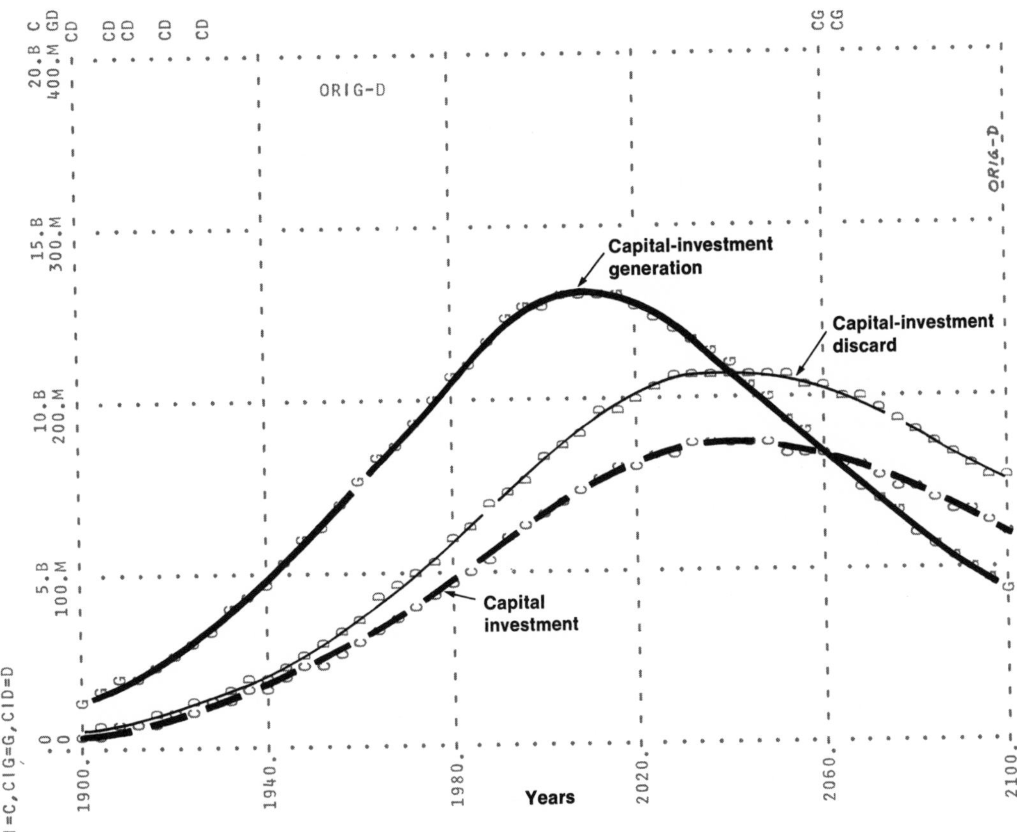

Figure 4-4 Original model as in Figure 4-1. The rate of capital-investment generation declines after 2010 but does not fall below the rate of capital-investment discard until 2040, at which time the level of capital investment begins to decline.

Figure 4-3 is the original system as in Figure 4-1 and shows a repeat of the curve for natural resources along with the natural-resource-usage rate. The peak of the usage curve comes at the point of maximum downward slope of the curve for natural resources. Natural resources are falling fastest when the usage rate is the highest.

Figure 4-4 is again from the original system and shows the generation and discard of capital investment and a repeat of the curve for capital investment. Until the year 2040, because capital-investment generation is greater than capital-investment discard, capital investment is rising. The peak of capital investment occurs where the generation rate and the discard rate cross and are equal. After year 2040, the discard exceeds the generation, and capital investment is falling.

Figures 4-1 through 4-4 should not be taken as a prediction of the course the world is now following. The assumed structure and values in the model have not been carefully enough examined to give assurance that the "original" model is the most likely one. Instead, the figure should be interpreted as one of the possible modes of behavior of the world system. One can argue that exhaustion of natural resources is not the most likely limitation on population growth. Actual stocks of natural resources may be greater than the 250-year supply that has been assumed here. Furthermore, science may make continuing substitutions to delay the impact of resource shortage.

If natural resources do not limit population growth and slow the pace of industrialization, however, some other force in the world system will eventually do so. If we wish to assume that natural resources will not fail, we can reduce the rate of their usage (or increase the assumed initial supply) to see which mode of behavior next appears.

4.3 Pollution Crisis

In a model of a social system, structure and numerical values can be changed to determine how the system behavior depends on the assumptions that have gone into the construction of the model. Some changes in the model are made to test sensitivity of the system to the original assumptions. Other changes explore altered policies in search of ways to improve performance of the real system. A third category of changes are made to search for various modes of behavior that the system can exhibit. The latter are useful to improve our understanding of the system with which we are working. This chapter examines three other ways (in addition to depletion of resources) by which the world system can suppress the growth of population.

In the preceding section the decline of natural resources halted the exponential growth of population and capital investment. Because the use of resources is continuous and irreversible, the continued decline of resources not only stopped growth but also reversed the trends and produced declines in world population and industrialization.

But natural resources may not be the most critical aspect of the world environment. It is easy to change the assumptions in the system model to reduce the dependence on natural resources.

Suppose we wish to assume that in the year 1970 the usage rate of natural resources were to be sharply curtailed without affecting any other part of the system. This might correspond to either an altered estimate of the actual rate of consumption relative to the available stocks in the earth, or it might correspond to technology finding ways to be less dependent on critical materials. Equation 9 in Section 3.9 provides for changing the natural-resource-usage rate normal NRUN1 at a specified time.

In Figure 4-5 the natural-resource-usage normal NRUN1 has been reduced to 25% of its original value in 1970. That is, if all other things were to be the same, the rate of consumption of resources would be a quarter of the previous value after 1970. Of course, other things do not remain the same. Natural-resource usage is still being affected by population and the material standard of living. The latter two continue to change and now move along a different time path than before because they respond to the consequences of a more slowly declining resource pool.

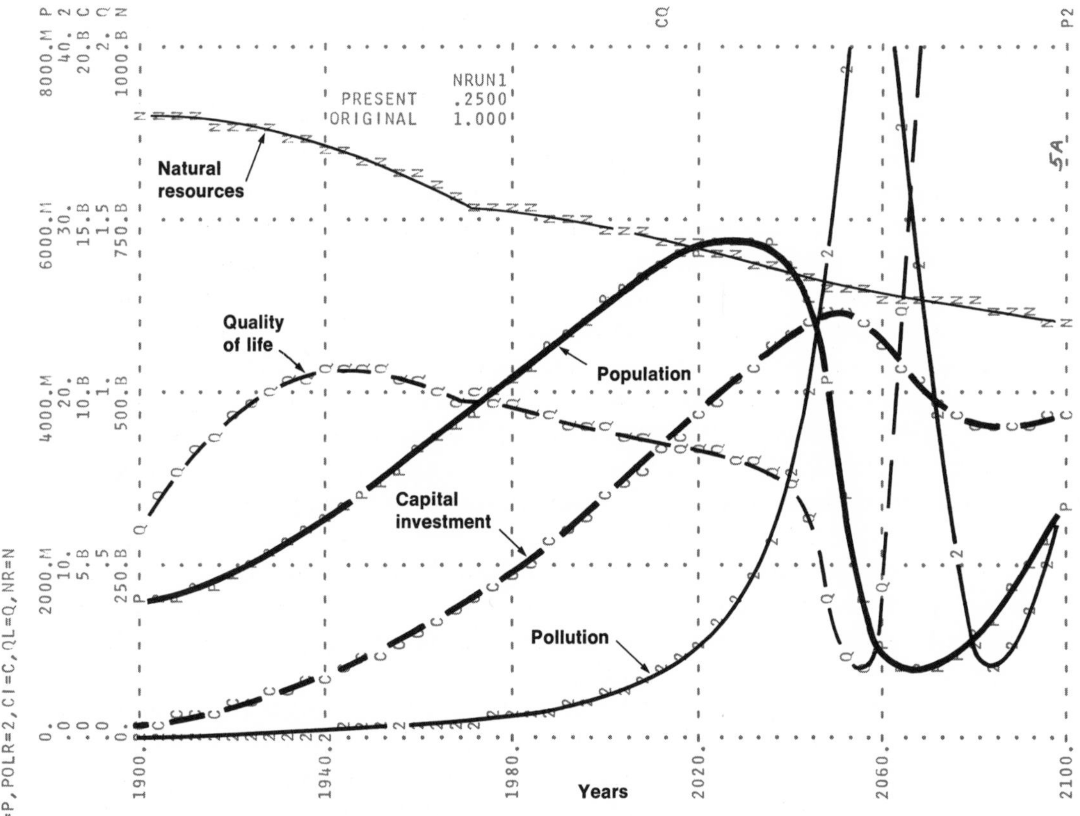

Figure 4-5 Reduced usage rate of natural resources leads to a pollution crisis.

The effect of reducing the demand for natural resources is to take one layer of restraint off the growth forces of the system. If natural resources no longer limit growth, the next growth-suppressing pressure will arise within the system.

Figure 4-5 shows pollution as the next barrier to appear. A pollution crisis lurks within the system. The regenerative upsurge of pollution can occur if no other pressure limits growth before pollution does so. Here pollution rises to more than 40 times the condition in 1970. Figure 4-5 should be compared with Figure 4-1 to see the effect of a reduced usage of natural resources which begins in 1970. Population continues for a longer time along its growth path. So does capital investment. Population and capital investment grow until they generate pollution at a rate beyond that which the environment can dissipate. When the pollution overloading occurs, pollution climbs steeply and continues to grow until it extinguishes the pollution-creating processes. This means a decline in population and capital investment until pollution generation falls below the pollution-absorption rate. In Figure 4-5 population drops in 20 years to one-sixth of its peak value.

The processes of pollution generation were not altered in the model by the reduced usage rate of natural resources. Some people argue that pollution is related directly to resource usage, but that seems only partially justified. A technology that is conserving rare metals might turn to chemicals and plastics with equivalent or high pollution danger.

Whether or not the population collapse would be as severe as in Figure 4-5 depends on which sector of the world population were most affected by the consequences of pollution. The highly aggregated model in Chapters 2 and 3 does not distinguish between industrialized and underdeveloped societies. In calculating the material standard of living, the total population is divided into the total capital investment. If population drops suddenly, the model formulation assumes that the capital is available and used by the remaining population. This is equivalent to assuming that the population decline from a pollution crisis afflicts those populations that are not using the capital investment. Such is probably not correct. It is most likely that the disruption of social systems and agriculture would occur in such a way that the industrialized societies would suffer the greatest population declines. If that were to happen, the pollution-generation processes would probably stop before the world population had dropped as far as shown in Figure 4-5. In other words, if the pollution crisis works its greatest hardship on the pollution-generating nations, the more numerous underdeveloped populations would survive with less reduction in population. Assumptions within the model will need to be carefully reexamined before substantial dependence is placed on the dynamics that follow the population peak.

It has been asserted by some who examine Figure 4-5 that the onset of the pollution crisis would cause people to reconsider their ways and to stop the pollution-generating processes before a catastrophe had occurred. But that may not happen. Reaction to the pollution crisis depends on its dynamic nature and on the steps that are necessary to stop it from taking the course shown in the figure. If, as will be suggested below, prevention requires a major cutback of industrial activity, the treatment will at first seem as serious as the disease. Pollution might indeed be recognized as destroying the developed countries, but so would shutting off industry, power plants, and fertilizer factories. The high density of population is possible only because of the industrialization. Without industrialization the population could not be sustained. A point may be reached where continuing the industrial process means a population collapse from pollution, while stopping the industrial process means a population collapse from failure of the technical support systems of the society. Faced with this dilemma, the most probable course of action is to wait and to hope that the pollution threat has been exaggerated. As a consequence of such indecision, the pollution cycle would continue.

In Figure 4-5 the quality of life dips suddenly and deeply as conditions become severe enough to drive down population. The rapid rise in quality of life after the year 2060 may be fictitious and is dependent on assumptions in the model that may not be valid for such severe conditions. The reasons for the rise in quality of life are shown in the next figure.

Figure 4-6 shows several system ratios for the same conditions as those in Figure 4-5. Material standard of living turns steeply upward when the population

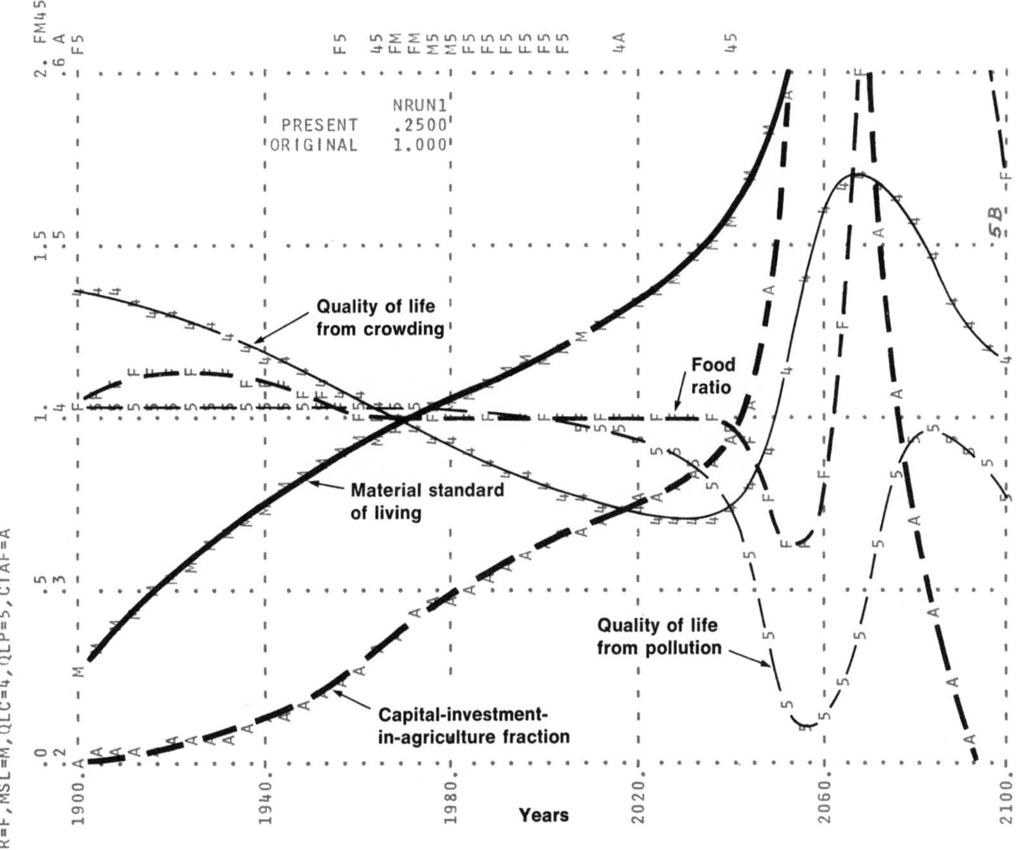

Figure 4-6 System ratios during the pollution mode of growth suppression.

begins to decline. This happens because of the assumption that all of the capital investment is available to and usable by the remaining population. Such might not be true under the catastrophic conditions that are depicted. If the population decline occurs mostly in the industrialized nations, capital investment and the remaining world population would be geographically separated. Also the differences in culture and education would prevent a population in an underdeveloped country from making effective use of capital investment that might be idle.

In Figure 4-6, as the food ratio begins to turn down, the capital-investment-in-agriculture fraction increases rapidly. This increase occurs because, while the material standard of living is high and places only slight demand on available capital investment, the food ratio is falling. The food ratio falls because of the detrimental influence of pollution on agriculture. Capital devoted to agriculture probably rises more quickly in the figure than could be accomplished in real life under such extreme circumstances of turmoil.

During the pollution crisis, the food ratio drops drastically because of the depression in agricultural output–a depression introduced by the food-from-pollution multiplier as described in Section 3.28, where it was asserted that a pollution ratio of 40 would depress food production to 20% of its value under 1970 pollution conditions. The rise in food ratio after the population collapse occurs because the reduced population has available the best agricultural lands and the remaining high capital investment in agriculture. Population, land, and capital investment might not be distributed so as to be mutually effective.

Quality of life from pollution dips, reasonably enough, in response to the 40-fold rise in pollution. Quality of life from crowding graphed in Figure 4-6, follows a path that is directly a result of the changes in population. Again, this implies that all land is available to the remaining population. Distributions other than the one implicitly assumed would keep the quality-of-life factors from rising so far at the right-hand end of the figure.

Figure 4-7 shows the dynamics of the pollution sector during the same time and conditions as those represented in Figure 4-5. Pollution rises steadily until about the year 2050 as a consequence of rising population and capital investment. Population decline which begins in 2040, does not immediately cause pollution generation to fall, for capital investment remains in existence and is assumed to be operated by the remaining population. As population declines, the capital-investment ratio as described in Section 3.23 rises, if the capital investment remains fixed. The pollution generation per capita as given by POLCM in Section 3.32 rises until it reaches its saturation region. Pollution generation then declines as population falls.

The regenerative pollution crisis is triggered when rising pollution no longer increases the rate of pollution absorption. In Figure 4-7 a point is reached at year 2030 where the pollution absorption no longer rises even though the total pollution load in the environment continues to increase. Figure 3-15 in Section 3.34 shows the critical point at a pollution ratio POLR of 10. The dashed line in the figure corresponds to a pollution-absorption time that is proportional to the pollution ratio. Moving along the dashed line, the pollution-absorption time doubles when the pollution doubles. In Section 3.33 the pollution-absorption rate POLA is proportional to pollution POL divided by the pollution-absorption time POLAT. If the pollution-absorption time POLAT rises proportional to pollution POL, the actual rate of pollution absorption is constant. This is seen in the section of Figure 4-7 for pollution absorption between the years 2030 and 2045. If the pollution-absorption time rises more rapidly than pollution, as it does in Figure 3-15 above a pollution ratio of 20, the rate of pollution absorption will fall as pollution continues to rise. The declining rate of pollution absorption is seen in Figure 4-7 between the years 2045 and 2060. In Figure 4-7 the pollution-absorption time rises to a peak of 13 years compared to the 1 year that was assumed for the 1970 average absorption time. It is the failure of the rate of pollution absorption to rise as total pollution rises which triggers the pollution crisis. Is such a phenomenon possible? It means that cleanup processes are

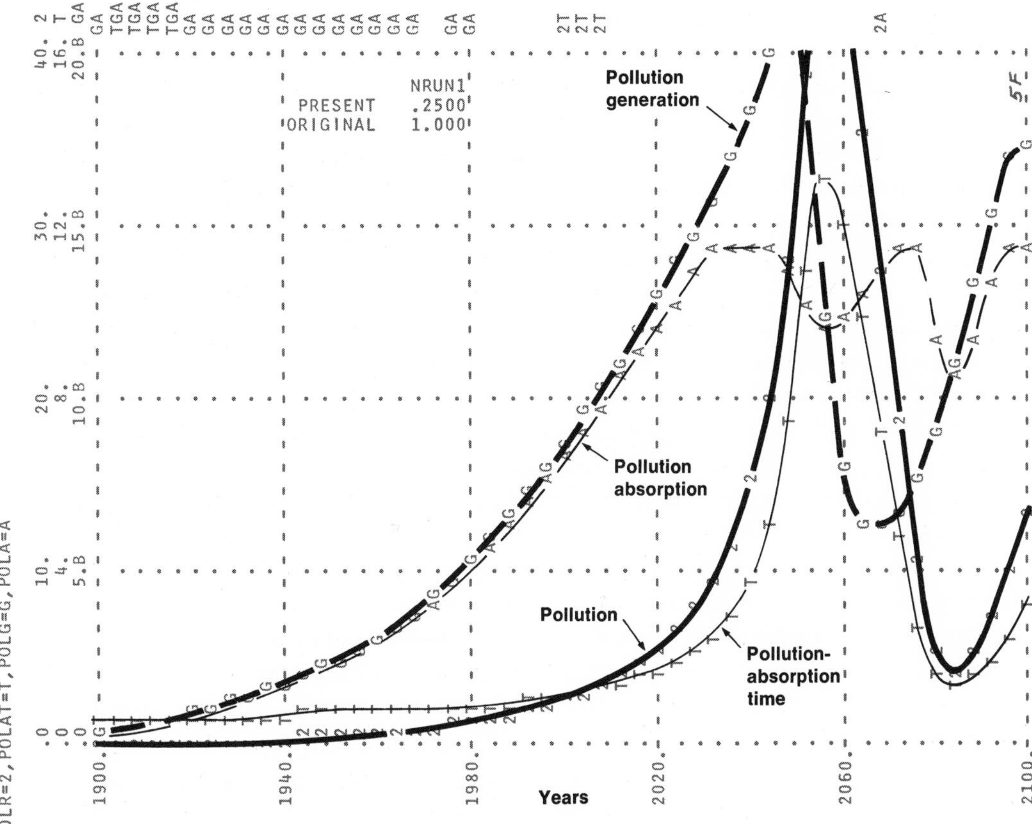

Figure 4-7 Dynamics of the pollution sector. A positive-feedback growth in pollution occurs when the pollution-absorption time increases faster than the pollution.

disrupted by the pollution itself. Many of the processes that have already been observed seem to have this character. The eutrophication of lakes progresses to a point where the purifying processes no longer keep up with rising contamination. In oceans and forests, sufficient interference with plant life and bacteria can slow their capability of restoring nature to its original balance. Our ecological systems show a high stability in the face of minor disturbances. Such stability is characteristic of multiple-loop nonlinear systems. But when pushed far enough, the equilibrium-seeking processes can break down. Beyond the breakdown point, cumulative and self-regenerating changes are possible. Figures 4-5 through 4-7 show such a breakdown when pollution load reaches a critical point.

At about year 2040 in Figure 4-7, a large gap has developed between pollution generation and pollution absorption. To stop the rise in pollution requires that the rate of pollution generation be dropped to less than the rate of pollution absorption. To be safely under the absorption rate, the generation rate would here need to be cut in half. That means discontinuing half of the industrial activity of the world. And only ten years elapse in the figure between 2030 when the rapid buildup starts and 2040 when only the most drastic action would suffice. It is doubtful that world organizations could respond with sufficient speed and vigor.

Figure 4-8 shows how birth and death rates are related to population. The conditions are the same as in Figure 4-5 in which the usage of natural resources is reduced from 1970 onward. Rising pollution after the year 2020 affects population in two ways. In addition to acting directly on birth and death rates, it acts indirectly by interfering with food production. The result is a steep rise in the death rate and a fall in the birth rate as the pollution crisis develops. The number of people dying per year doubles between 2030 and 2050. About year 2060 the birth rate drops to a very low value, partly because the population itself has fallen to a small fraction of its maximum and partly because of severe conditions.

Whether or not the reactions as shown during and after the pollution crisis would occur under actual conditions depends on the validity of the implicit assumptions about distribution of population, capital investment, and land as discussed earlier. The death rate in Figure 4-8 at year 1900 starts equal to or above birth rate and represents a small transient readjustment of initial conditions that are not properly balanced for the growth phase. Such questions raised by the behavior of a model system cause us to reexamine and improve the model. Further improvements are to be a part of programs now in progress.

Figure 4-5 teaches a fundamental lesson about complex systems. When one pressure or difficulty is alleviated, the result may be merely to substitute a new problem for the old. Often the new mode is less desirable than the old. In particular, the industrialized societies have come to depend on technology to solve their problems. This succeeded when technology was improving so rapidly that it could exploit geographical space and natural resources faster than the population could increase. But now, as technology reaches the point of diminishing returns and begins to run short on space and resources, the technological "solution" may more and more be only a substitution of one crisis for another. In this section we have seen that the natural-resource shortage was solved only to be replaced by the pollution crisis. Of the two, the pollution crisis is more traumatic than the gradual pressures created by the resource shortage. Of course, conflict for possession of resources could reverse that conclusion.

This process of a solution creating a new problem has defeated many of our past national and world programs and will continue to do so unless we devote more effort to understanding the dynamic behavior of our social systems.

It becomes increasingly important to look beyond short-term solutions and ask about ultimate consequences. Where will the new pressures arise? Over the last two centuries it appears that improved technology and better medical treatment have been major contributors to the "population explosion." A humanitarian medical program may in the long run subject a much-expanded world population to the ultimate pressures of over-population. In historical perspective we may see that many more people suffer in the future so that a few can benefit in the present. What is the proper trade-off?

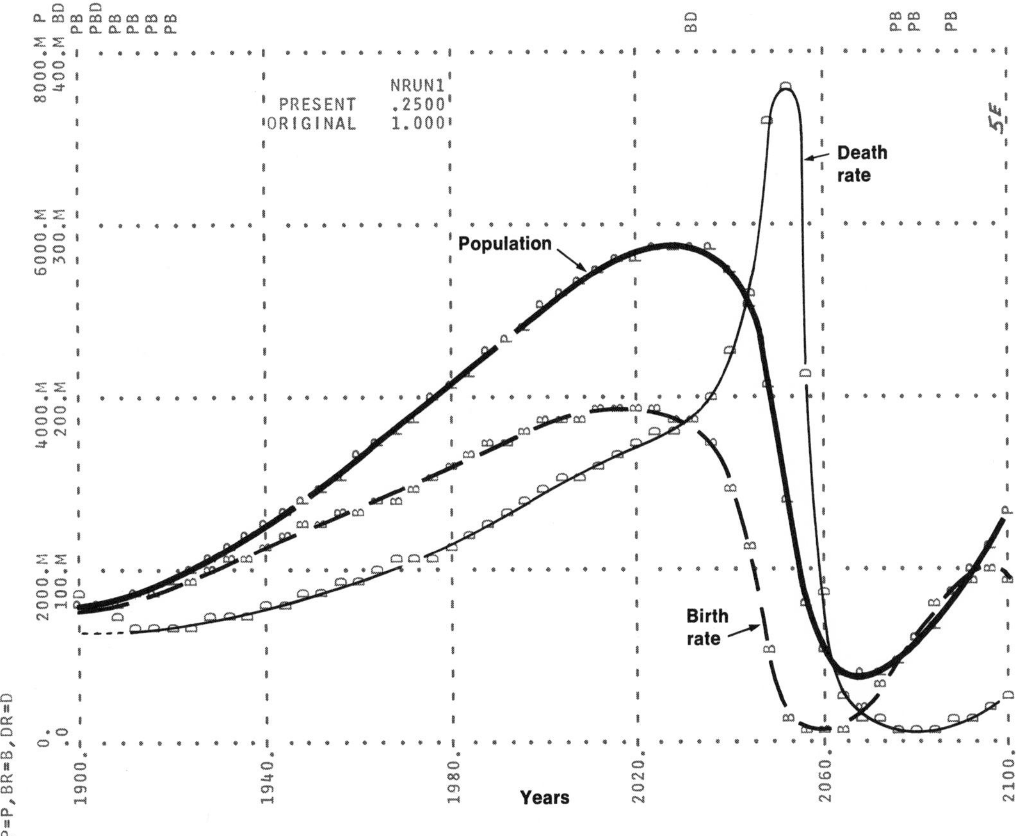

Figure 4-8 Population sector during the pollution mode.

4.4 Crowding

Section 4.2 discussed the mode in which growth was suppressed by falling natural resources. In Section 4.3 the usage rate of resources was reduced enough that pollution appeared as the next limit to growth. Now, if the effects of natural resources and pollution are both removed from the model, the third limit to growth can be examined.

The natural-resource-usage rate normal NRUN1 will be set to zero, and the pollution normal POLN1 will be set to 0.1 at year 1970. This means that no resources will be used after 1970 and that the pollution rate is reduced to 10% of what it would have been for the same system conditions. These are unrealistic assumptions because they create no cost or depressing effects on other parts of the system. The result is shown in Figure 4-9.

Population rises to about 9.7 billion, which corresponds to a crowding ratio CR of 2.65 times the 1970 world population. By the year 2060 the quality of life has fallen far enough to reduce the rate of rise in population. Population is essentially stable by 2200.

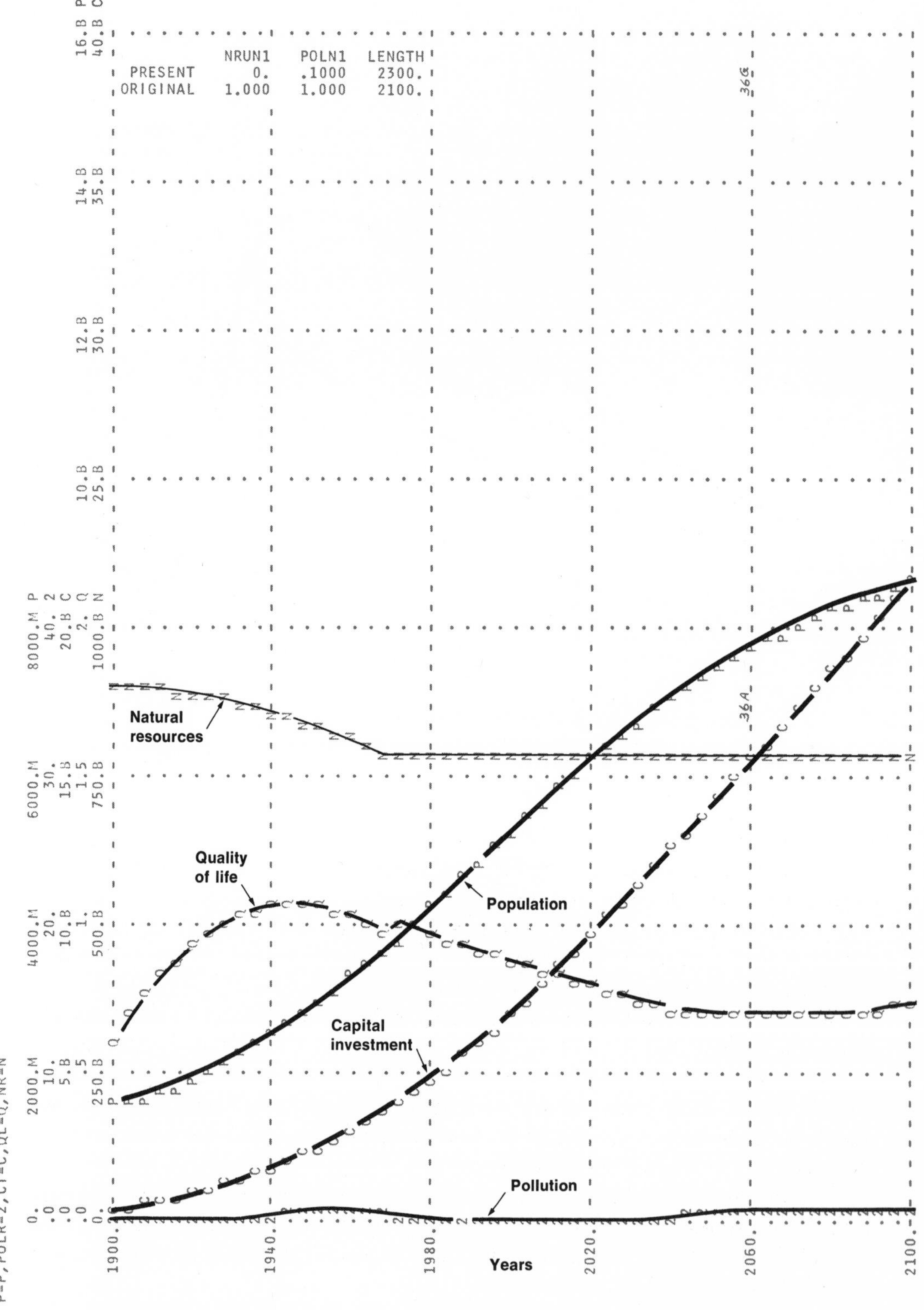

Figure 4-9 Growth suppressed by crowding when natural resources and pollution are inactive.

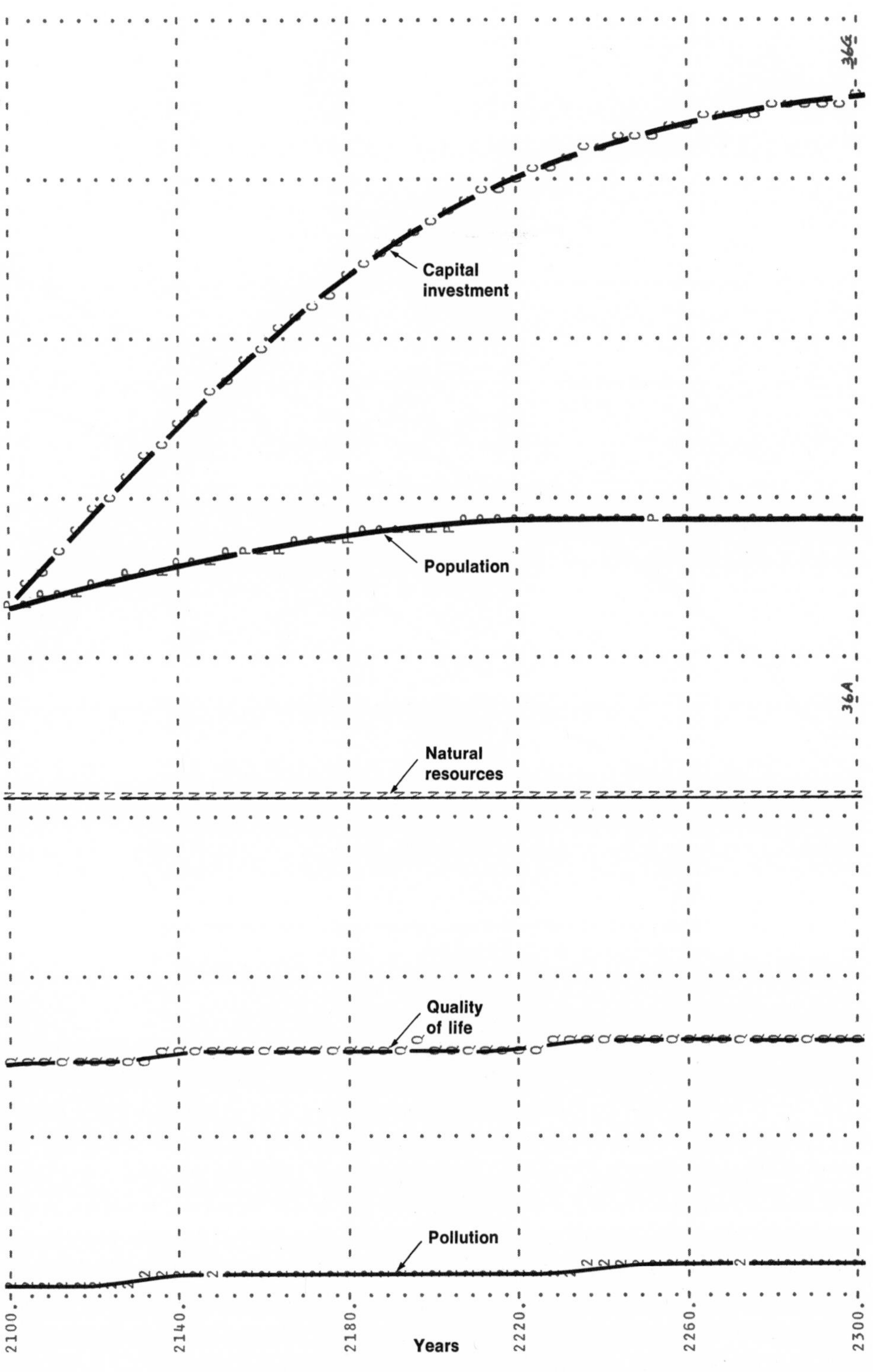

Figure 4-9 (continued)

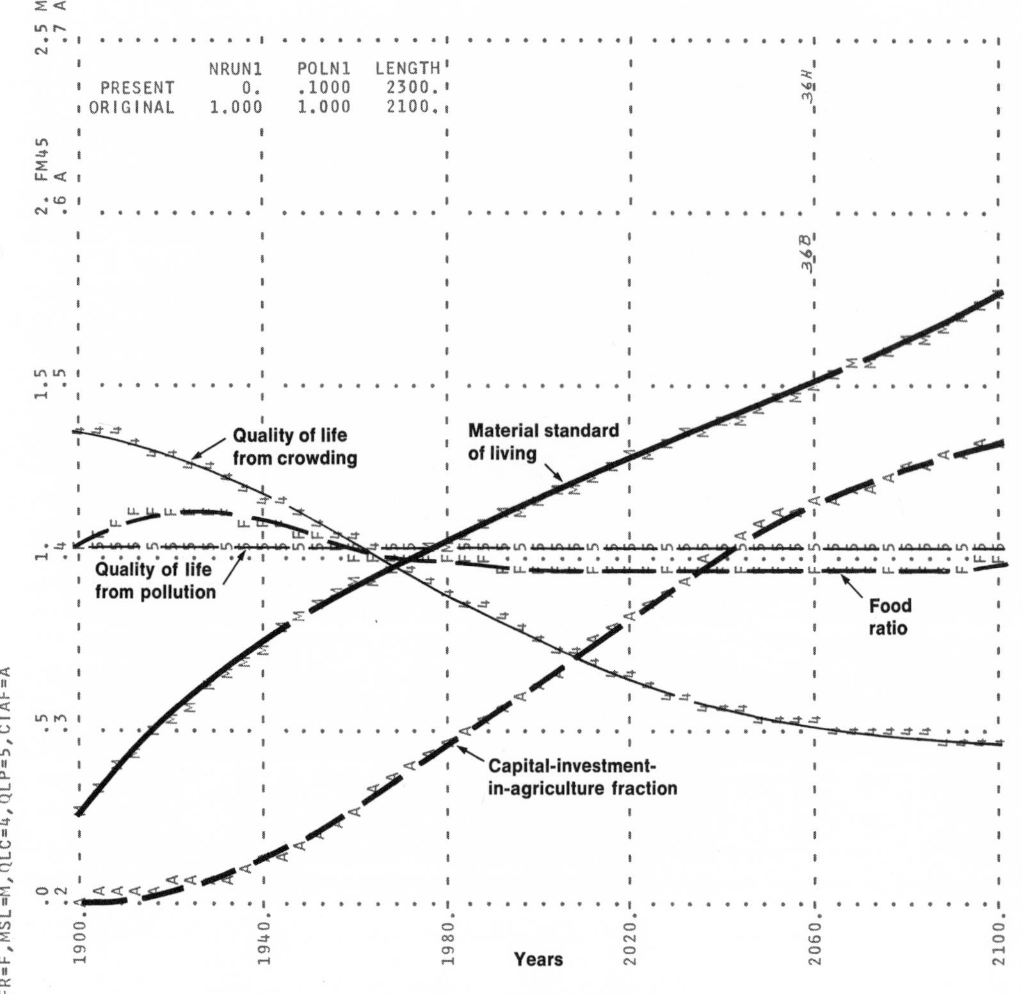

Figure 4-10 System ratios when growth is suppressed by crowding.

In Figure 4-9 the capital investment rises to 38 billion units to yield a capital-investment ratio CIR of 3.9 times the 1970 capital investment per person. This, of course, is possible only because of the assumptions that resources are unlimited and pollution has been suppressed. But Figure 4-10 shows that the high capital-investment ratio is only partly available to raise the material standard of living, which rises to only 2.3 times the 1970 value. The greater crowding and the increased demand for food, coupled with the necessity of using less productive agricultural land, have diverted more capital investment to food production. The capital-investment-in-agriculture fraction CIAF has risen from 0.28 in 1970 to 0.55 in 2300. The increase in capital devoted to agriculture is here able to maintain the food ratio near unity for the entire interval of time.

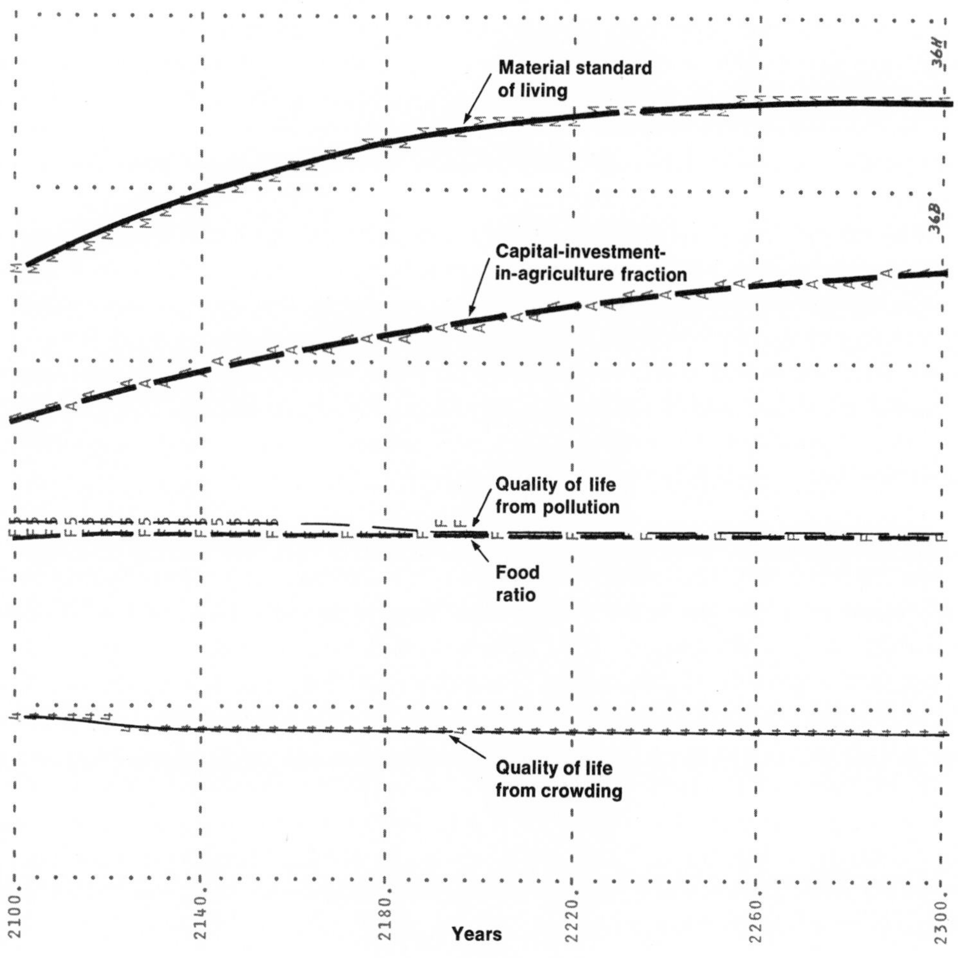

Figure 4-10 (continued)

As capital investment grows, capital-investment discard CID grows proportionately as a result of wear-out and deterioration. At the same time, the incentive to accumulate further capital begins to abate as seen in Section 3.26. The result is an equilibrium above which capital ceases to grow.

The crowding sector of the model has no regenerative processes of the kind seen in the pollution sector. Neither are there any time delays between crowding and the effect on population growth. These omissions of factors that might be found in actual systems accounts for the smooth growth of population and capital investment in Figure 4-9 and the eventual approach to a steady equilibrium. If time delays existed, the curves could rise above their equilibrium values and fluctuate around the equilibrium values. If regenerative processes were included, one could expect the same kind of population collapse seen in Section 4.3 as caused by the pollution sector. Such regenerative processes are actually to be anticipated in the crowding sector as well. If crowding were to lead to international conflict and an atomic war, population would probably drop back below the equilibrium point and then grow again. If crowding contributes to massive epidemics of disease, population could show an instability around equilibrium. A more elaborate model would make these other dynamic modes possible.

Figures 4-9 and 4-10 show the mode produced by the crowding limit that is inherent in the effect of crowding on population as asserted in Sections 3.14 and 3.16. Crowding also operates indirectly on population through the food sector as seen in Figure 2-1 and in Section 3.19 and 3.20. Quality of life drops to about 0.8 of its 1970 value and is a combination of a rising quality from a higher material standard of living and a falling quality from greater crowding. The effects on quality of life from food production and pollution (which was suppressed in Figures 4-9 and 4-10) are almost unchanged.

4.5 Food Shortage

In Section 4.4 the effects of resource depletion and of pollution were suppressed to show the influence of crowding on growth. Now, if the effect of crowding is also eliminated, food shortage will become the limiting factor in stopping the growth of population. To make this change in the model, we keep the values NRUN1 and POLN1 as they were in the preceding section and suppress the effects of crowding on the birth and death rates. The latter adjustment can be made by changing the tables in Sections 3.14 and 3.16 so that they have no effect as crowding increases. The effect of these tables can be eliminated by changing the values to 1 for all crowding ratios above 1. Then, regardless of how far the crowding rises, the crowding multipliers for birth and death rates will have a value of 1. The result is shown in Figure 4-11.

Note to the Reader: This page has been left blank to accommodate the two-page diagram which follows.

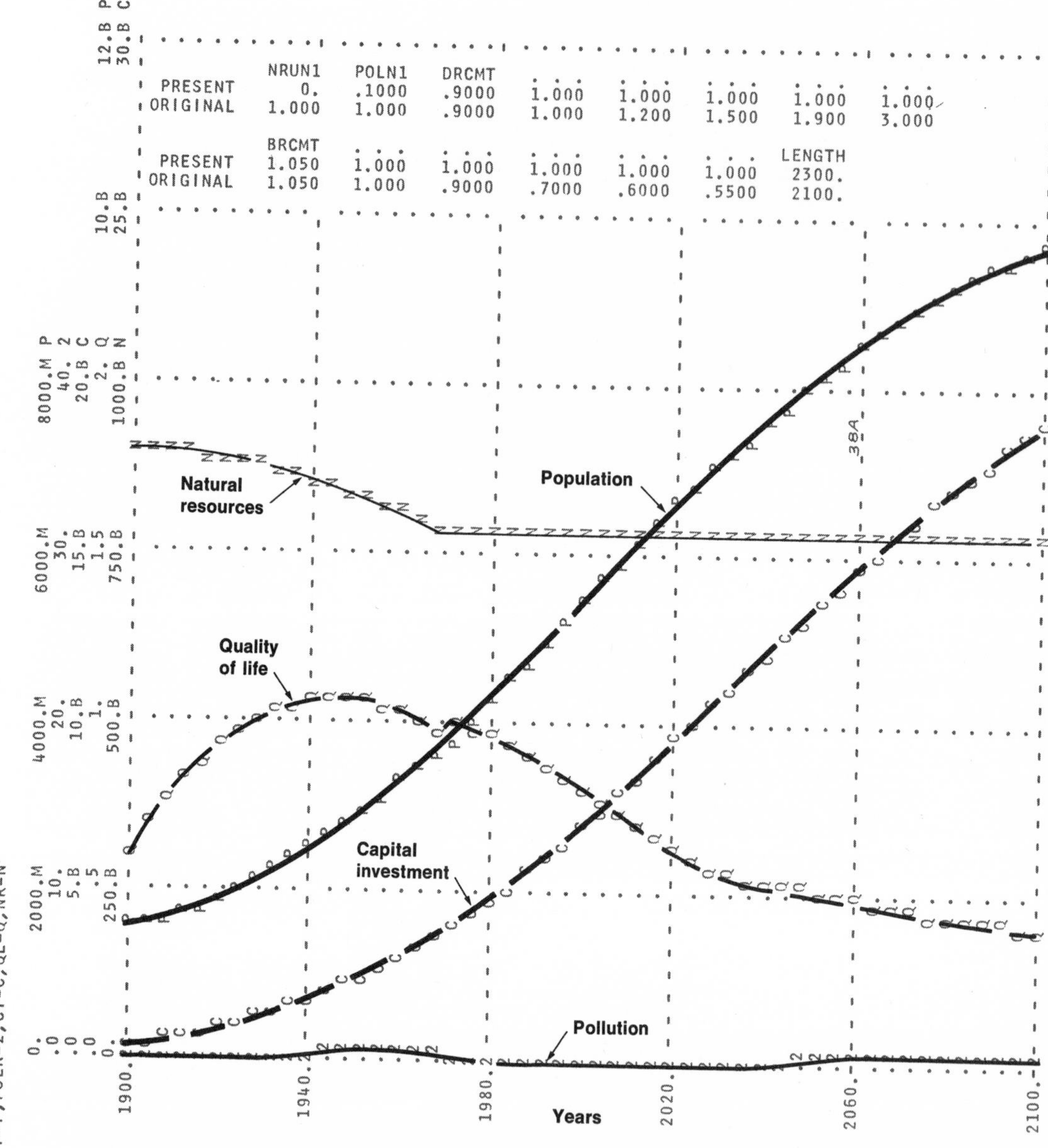

Figure 4-11 Food shortage as the only remaining pressure to stop population growth.

Population rises to 10.8 billion people, which is only moderately higher than the 9.7 billion in Section 4.4. A comparison of Figure 4-11 with Figure 4-9 shows a different kind of equilibrium balance between population and capital

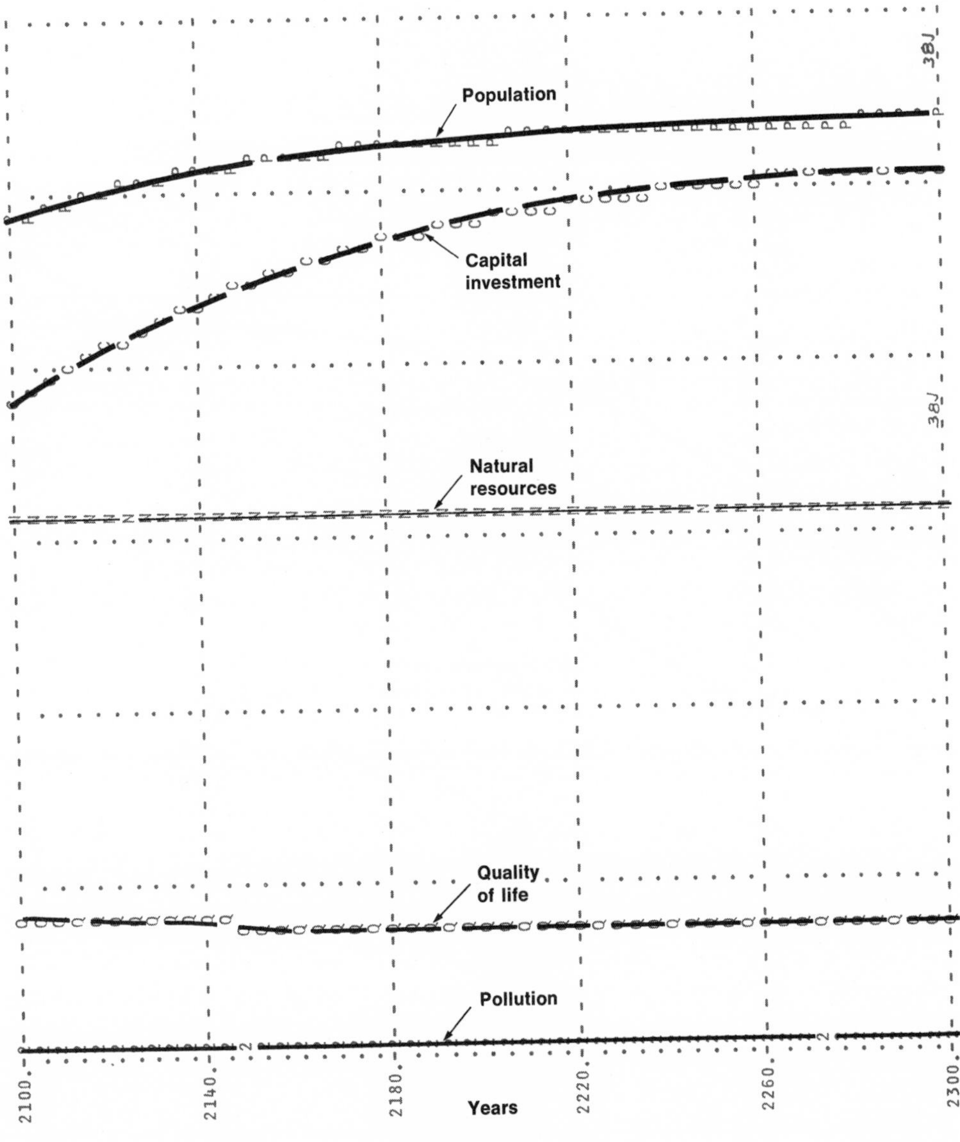

Figure 4-11 (continued)

investment. In Figure 4-11 population rises more steeply at first. This lowers the material standard of living and the ability to accumulate capital. The demands for food pull capital into food production, leaving not enough in the material-standard-of-living sector to regenerate capital to as high a level as in Figure 4-9.

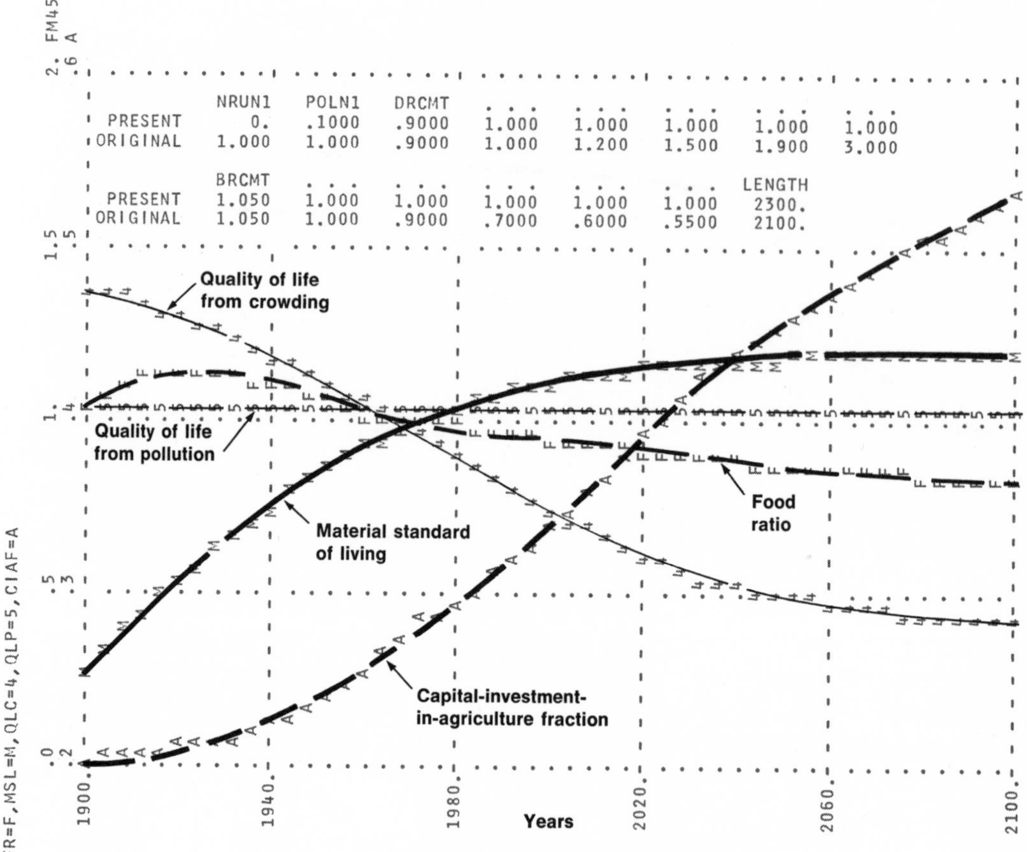

Figure 4-12 System ratios during the food-shortage mode.

Figure 4-12 shows a lower material standard of living and a lower food ratio than in the preceding section. The quality of life in Figure 4-11 is therefore substantially lower.

Because the crowding is no longer having a direct effect on birth and death rates, other unfavorable factors must become powerful enough to compensate in stopping the growth of population. Here this occurs by a reduction in the food ratio. The material standard of living also falls but has little effect because it causes birth rate and death rate both to increase as it falls, and these nearly compensate. The fall in food ratio is substantial, declining to 0.77. This is sufficient to stop the rise in population. Regardless of the assumptions about the sensitivity of birth and death rates to the food ratio, if all other influences on growth are removed, the population will rise by as much as necessary to generate the degree of food shortage that is needed to suppress growth.

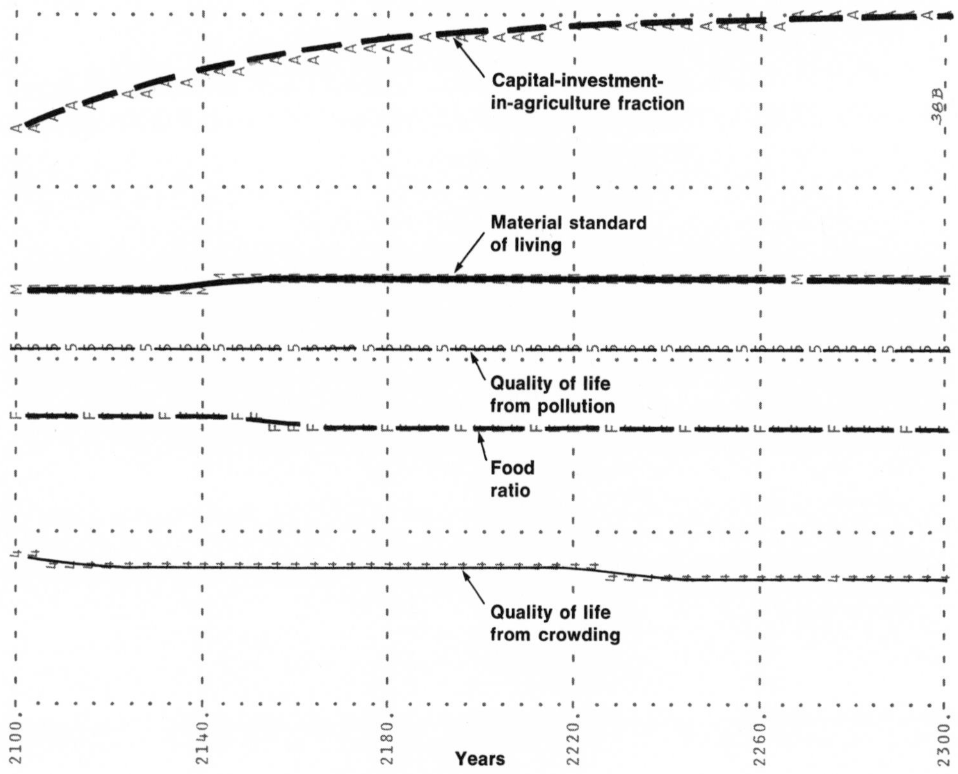

Figure 4-12 (continued)

5 Obvious Responses Will Not Suffice

The dynamic characteristics of complex social systems frequently mislead people. Some of these characteristics were first identified in the work at M.I.T. with corporate and urban systems and now appear again in the way people interact with the world system to sustain a series of crises.

Initially the characteristics of social systems began to emerge from the modeling of corporate policy structures. Often we have gone into a corporation which is having severe and well-known difficulties. The difficulties can be major and obvious like falling market share, or low profitability, or instability of employment. Such difficulties are known throughout the company and by anyone outside who reads the management press. The first step in understanding such a company is to discuss with people in key decision points the actions they are taking to solve the problem. Generally speaking we find that people perceive correctly their immediate environment. They know what they are trying to accomplish. They know the crises which will force certain actions. They are sensitive to the power structure of the organization, to traditions, and to their own personal goals and welfare. In general, when circumstances are conducive to frank disclosure, people can state what they are doing and can give rational reasons for their action. In a troubled company, people are usually trying in good conscience and to the best of their abilities to solve the major difficulties. From such an organization one can take the policies that are well-known and are being followed at the various points in the organization. The policies are being followed on the presumption that they will alleviate the difficulties. These policies are then combined into a computer model to show the consequences of how the policies interact with one another. In many instances it then emerges that the known policies describe a system which actually causes the troubles. In other words, the known and intended practices of the organization are often fully sufficient to create the difficulty, regardless of what happens outside the company or in the marketplace. In fact, a downward spiral develops in which the presumed solution makes the difficulty worse and thereby causes redoubling of the presumed solution so that matters become still worse.

The same downward spiral frequently develops in national government and at the level of world affairs. Judgment and debate lead to programs that appear to be sound. Commitment increases to the apparent solutions. If the presumed solutions actually make matters worse, the process by which this happens is not evident. So, when the troubles increase, the efforts are intensified that are actually worsening the problems.

The intuitively obvious "solutions" to social problems are apt to fall into one of several traps set by the character of complex systems. First, an attempt to relieve one set of symptoms may only create a new mode of system behavior that also has unpleasant consequences. Second, the attempt to produce short-term improvement often sets the stage for a long-term degradation. Third, the local goals of a part of a system often conflict with the objectives of the larger system. Fourth, people are often led to intervene at points in a system where little leverage exists and where effort and money have but slight effect. These four ways in which a social system can mislead us will now be discussed in more detail.

The first kind of system response, wherein a new trouble appears as a result of solving the old, has already been illustrated in Chapter 4. The first mode exhibited by the world system in Section 4.2 developed a population decline and a falling quality of life because natural resources were being exhausted. By assuming a technological solution, the system was freed from dependence on resources in Section 4.3 but a worse kind of crisis developed—the runaway pollution mode. Then in Section 4.4 pollution was assumed to be controllable and crowding became severe enough to drive down the quality of life until population no longer rose. Then in a third attempt to relieve the pressures on the system, crowding was removed in Section 4.5 as a factor in birth and death rates, implying that psychological adjustments could be made to high-density living. The last and ultimate barrier, a food shortage, developed. Each attempt to eliminate a pressure within the system led to a new pressure.

As to the second characteristic, social systems usually exhibit fundamental conflict between the short-term and long-term consequences of a policy change. A policy which produces improvement in the short run is usually one which degrades the system in the long run. Short run and long run must be defined in terms of the dynamic responses in the system of interest. In corporate affairs, short run might be one to three years and long run beyond five years. In urban or national issues, short run could be a decade, while long run might be twenty years or more. In world dynamics, short run is several decades, and long run is fifty years to several centuries. Policies and programs which produce long-run improvement may initially depress the behavior of a system. This is especially treacherous. The short run is more visible and more compelling. It speaks loudly for immediate attention. But a series of actions all aimed at short-run improvement can eventually burden a system with long-run depressants so severe that even heroic short-run measures no longer suffice. Many of the problems which the world faces today are the eventual result of short-run measures taken over the last century. Industrialization has raised the standard of living but now leads to pollution. Improvements in medicine and sanitation facilities improved health and reduced death rate but has led to the pressures from rising population. Greater capital investment and more intensive use of land in agriculture have increased food output in the short run but in the long run have destroyed the productivity of vast land areas by erosion and salt contamination.

As for the third characteristic of complex systems, there is usually a conflict between the goals of a subsystem and the welfare of the broader system. We see this in urban systems where the goal of a city is to expand and to raise its quality of life. But, as the city strives to meet its goals, the nation encounters increased population, industrialization, pollution, and demand on food supply. The broader social system of a country or the world requires that the goals of the urban areas be curtailed and that the pressures of such curtailment become high enough to keep the urban areas and population within the bounds that are satisfactory to the larger system of which the city is a part. Nations strive for economic growth, higher standard of living, more food, and even increased population. If they succeed, as they may well do, the result will be to deepen the distress of the world as a whole and eventually to deepen the crises in the individual nations themselves. We are at the point where higher pressures in the present are necessary if insurmountable pressures are to be avoided in the future.

As a fourth characteristic, social systems are inherently insensitive to most policy changes that people select in an effort to alter behavior. In fact, a social system draws attention to the very points at which an attempt to intervene will fail. Human experience, which has been developed from contact with simple systems, leads us to look close to the symptoms of trouble for a cause. But when we look, we are misled because the social system presents us with an apparent cause that is plausible according to the lessons we have learned from simple systems, although this apparent cause is usually a coincident occurrence that, like the trouble symptom itself, is being produced by the feedback-loop dynamics of a larger system. In the world system, birth control is likely to be one of those apparent control points that in fact lack leverage for change. At the detailed demographic level, so many factors impinge on birth rate that an active program of birth control will be largely defeated by relaxation of controls that previously existed. As another example, efforts to reduce hunger by greater food production will generally fail unless there are simultaneous counterforces sufficiently large to prevent the population rising to match the new level of food availability.

5.1 Increased Capital-Investment Generation

Increased industrialization, created by a higher rate of capital investment, may be one of those system interventions that eventually succeeds only in exchanging one system stress for another. In Figure 4-1 the quality of life began to decline after 1950. How might the earlier rise in quality of life be sustained? One way to attempt this, and it is the way the world is now choosing, would be to increase

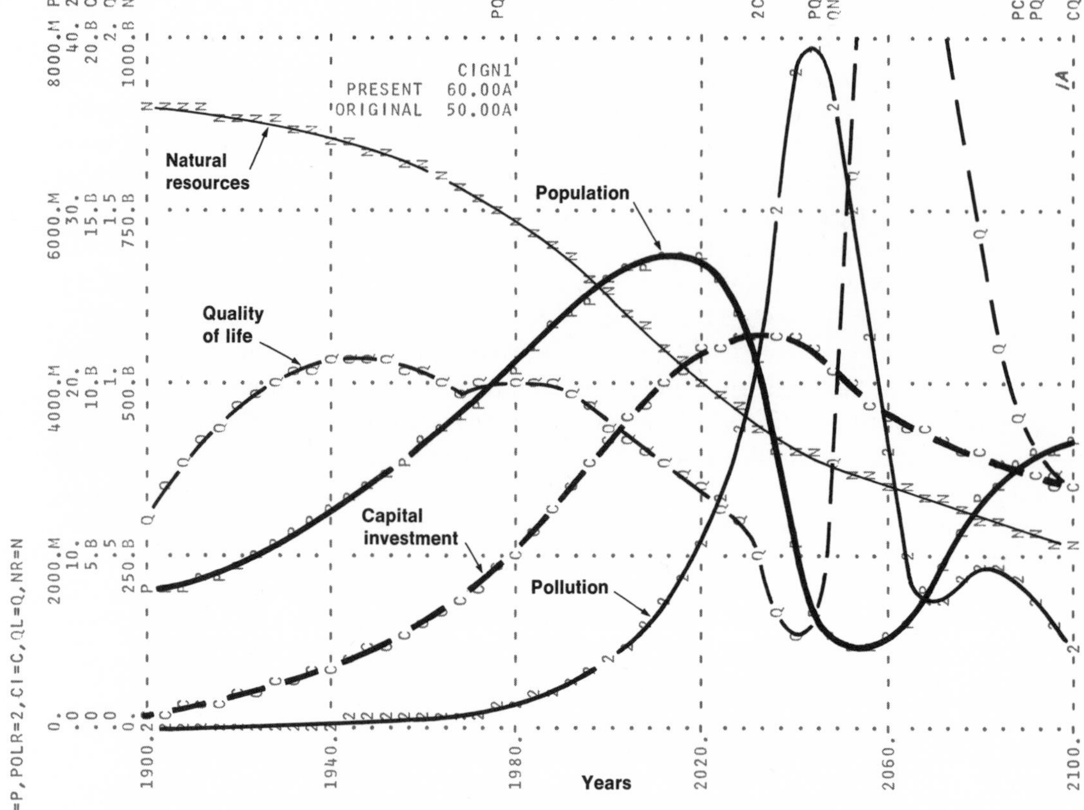

Figure 5-1 Higher capital-investment generation triggers the pollution crisis.

the rate of industrialization by raising the rate of capital investment.

In a system model one can easily make changes in assumed governing policies in the system to observe the consequences of modifying the system rates of activity. The answer from within the model context can be obtained in a few minutes and at negligible cost. The relevance of the answer to real life depends on the adequacy of the model.

Figure 5-1 shows the result of increasing by 20% in 1970 the coefficient for capital-investment generation normal CIGN1 (see Section 3.25). This means that, for any given set of conditions, the rate of capital accumulation will be 20% greater than it was in the original model.

As a result, the pollution crisis reappears. In Figure 4-5 the pollution crisis occurred because natural resources were depleted slowly enough that population and industrialization exceeded the pollution-absorption capability of the earth. Here in Figure 5-1 the pollution crisis occurs because industrialization is rushed and reaches the pollution limit before the industrial society has existed long enough to deplete resources.

In Figure 5-1 an "obvious" desirable change in policy has caused troubles worse than the ones that were originally to be corrected. This consequence of a higher rate of capital investment demonstrates how an apparently desirable change in a social system can have unexpected and even disastrous results. Quality of life does turn up for a time after 1970 but, by 2020, has fallen as low as in Figure 4-1 and immediately thereafter falls steeply.

Figure 5-1 should make us cautious about rushing into programs on the basis of short-term humanitarian impulses. The eventual result can be anti-humanitarian. What is the proper trade-off between benefits in the near future in exchange for distress in the more distant future?

The effect of a corrective program can be along an entirely different direction than was originally expected. Suppressing one symptom may only cause trouble to burst forth at another point. Intuition, judgment, and argument are not reliable guides to the consequences of an intervention into system behavior. Only an adequate dynamic analysis of the system can show the consequence of a changed policy for managing the system.

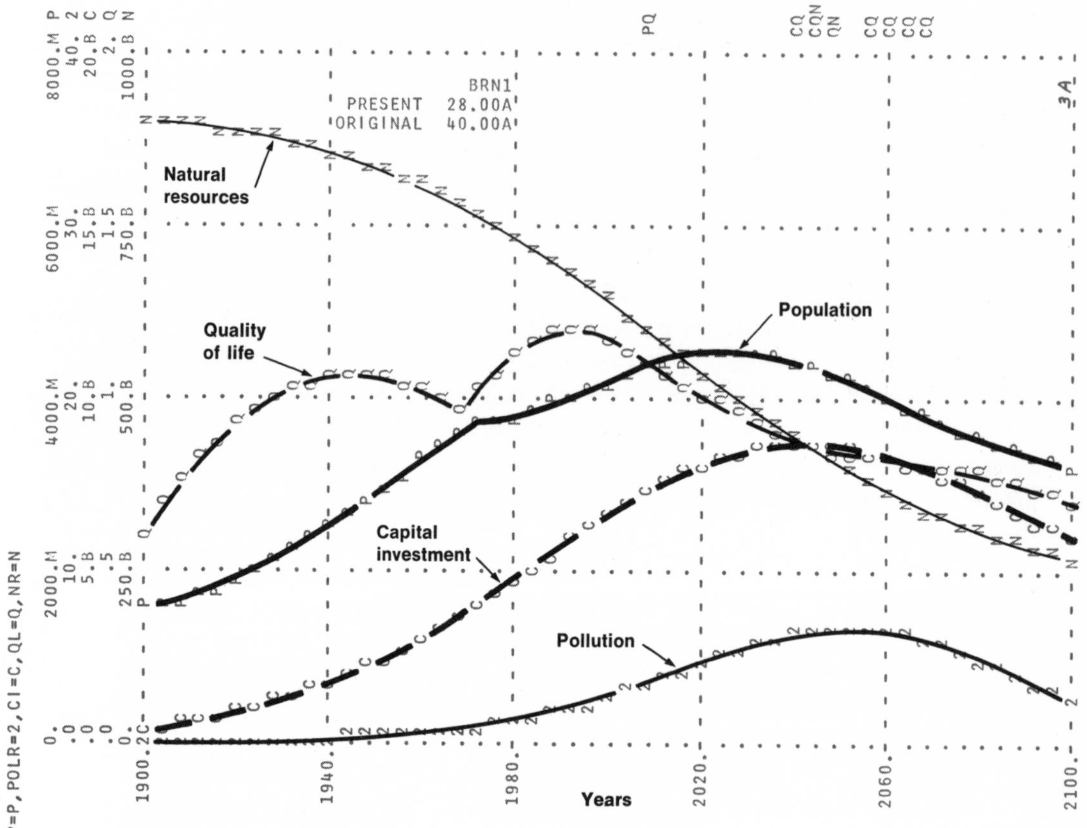

Figure 5-2 Lower birth rate does not affect suppression of growth by falling natural resources.

5.2 Reduced Birth Rate

Within the context of a global dynamic system, what result might we expect from birth-control programs? Will they be effective, or will they fall into one of the failure categories so common to programs that attempt to intervene in the behavior of social systems? Will a birth-control program create a new set of problems? Or will it represent only a short-term improvement? Or will it turn out to be in conflict with some broader system goal? Or will it be a low-leverage point with little effect? Probably it is the latter.

In Figure 5-2 the birth rate normal BRN1 (see Section 3.2) has been reduced from 0.040 to 0.028 in 1970. This is sufficient to eliminate the 1.2% population growth rate that had existed from 1900 to 1970 if the system does not compensate for the birth-control program. A comparison with Figure 4-1 shows but slight change in the ultimate outcome.

In Figure 5-2 there is a brief pause in the growth of population after the birth-control program is started in 1970. But during the pause, capital investment continues to increase. A comparison of Figure 5-3 with 4-2 shows that the material standard of living has risen and the food ratio has increased during the decade

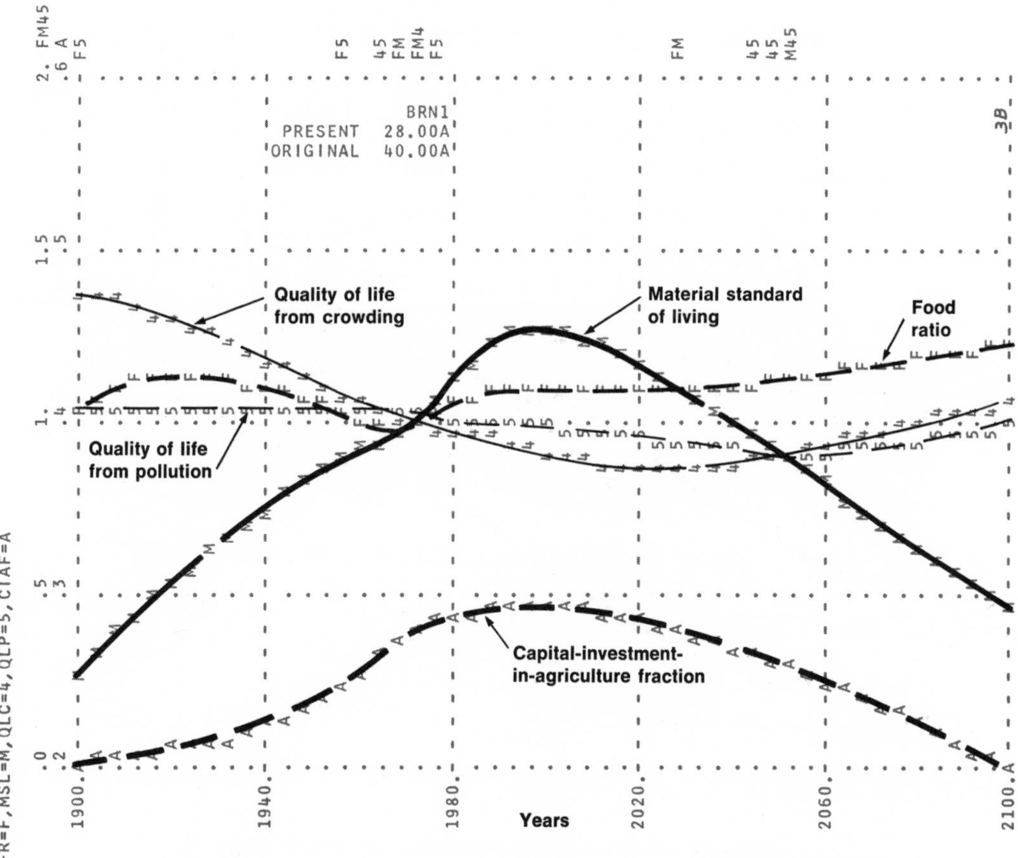

Figure 5-3 Ratios for the same condition of lower birth rate as in Figure 5-2.

that population was stable. The quality of life rose during the interval and, in effect, reduced the internal system pressures that had previously been limiting the rise of population.

The rate of increase of population depends on a combination of many influences. But the influences interact between themselves in such a way that reducing one is apt to cause others to increase and thereby partially compensate for the reduction. A birth-control program is one of the many influences on birth rate. When the emphasis on birth control is increased, the immediate effect may be to depress birth rate, but in the longer run the other influences within the system change in a direction that tends to defeat the program. Figure 5-2 shows that after the system readjusts internally in reaction to the imposed birth-control program, the population resumes its upward trend. Because the system is still limited by falling natural resources, the population peaks and then declines as before. The effect of the program has been to delay the rise in population for a short time but to leave unchanged the dominant mode of growth limitation, which was the falling natural resources.

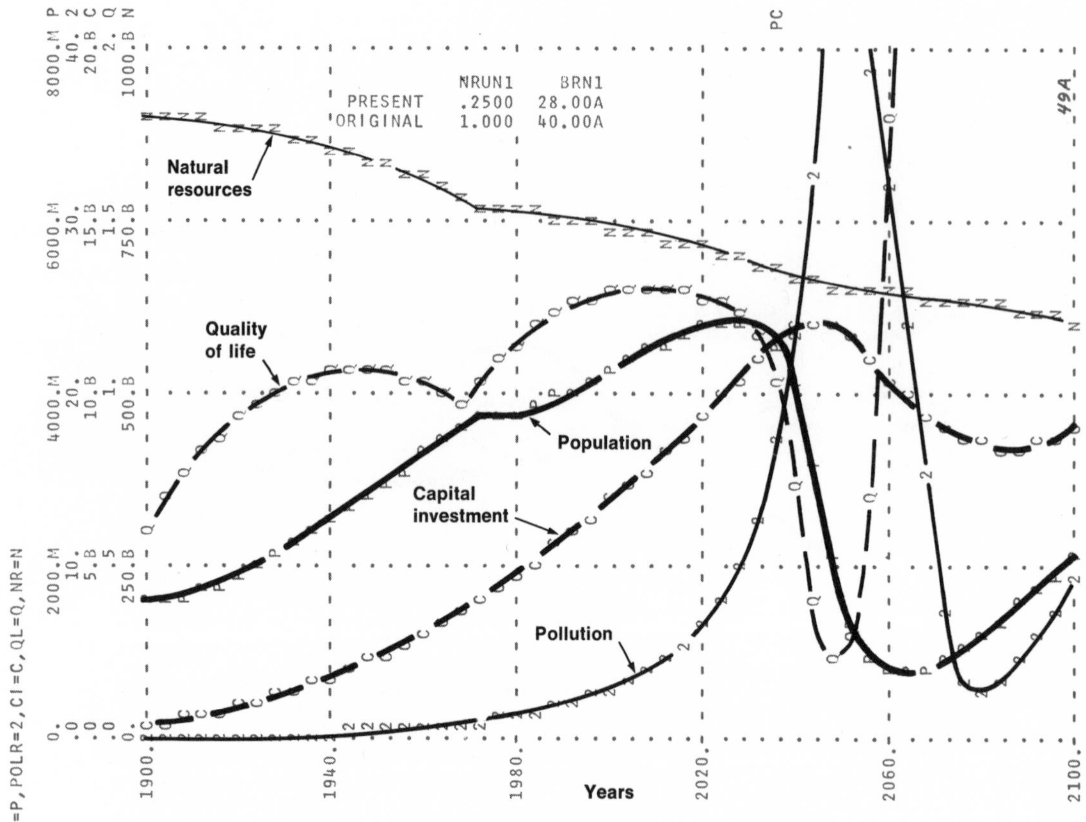

Figure 5-4 Reduced birth rate still leads to the pollution crisis.

The increase in the quality of life appearing in Figure 5-2 after the introduction of the birth-control program is probably a consequence of the simplicity of this world model. The probable reasons for less effect on quality of life in the real-world system will be discussed at the end of this section.

But would a birth-control program be effective in forestalling undesirable modes other than the depletion of resources? What effect would such a program have on an impending pollution crisis? The question can be explored in comparison to the behavior already seen in Figure 4-5 where the pollution crisis developed when the usage rate of natural resources was reduced.

Figure 5-4 shows the combined effect of a lowered usage of resources and a reduced birth rate. Natural-resource usage normal NRUN1 is reduced to 25% of its original value, and birth rate normal BRN1 is reduced to 0.028 or 70% of its original value. The ultimate result is similar to that in Figure 4-5. In Figure 5-4 population pauses until a rise in the food ratio (not shown) and the quality of life starts the population climbing again. Although the increase in population has been delayed and slowed somewhat, capital investment continues to accumulate at about the same rate as in Figure 4-5. Load on the environment is more closely

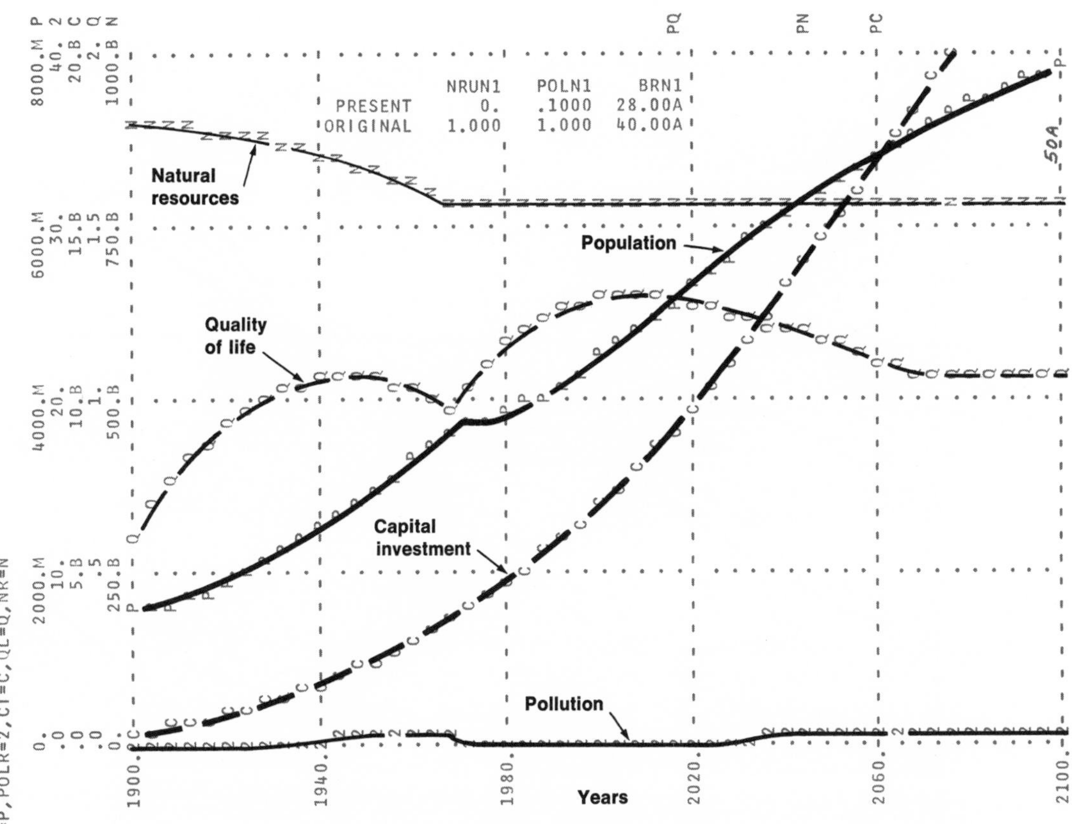

Figure 5-5 With resource depletion and pollution suppressed, population still climbs even with a 30% reduction in "normal" birth rate.

related to industrialization than to population, and the pollution crisis occurs at about the same point in time as it did in Figure 4-5. The birth-control program has not stopped the increase in population; nor has it prevented the pollution crisis. For a brief period it did raise the quality of life, but this gain would probably be replaced in an actual system by shifts in psychological and sociological variables as discussed below.

Figures 5-2 through 5-4 examine the introduction of a birth-control program not long before an impending crisis is already destined to reverse the rising population. Now we examine the dynamics of population control when crowding is the barrier to continued growth. This is not realistic, of course, for the questions of natural resources and pollution cannot be swept aside in actuality by just changing a model coefficient. However, it will be instructive to examine the ultimate test of population limitation in this system. We use Figure 4-9 as the point of reference in which the use of resources and the generation of pollution have been suppressed from 1970 onward. Also in 1970, BRN1 is now reduced to 0.028 to yield Figure 5-5. Quality of life rises substantially as a result of increased material standard of living and increased food per capita. The effect of food is probably

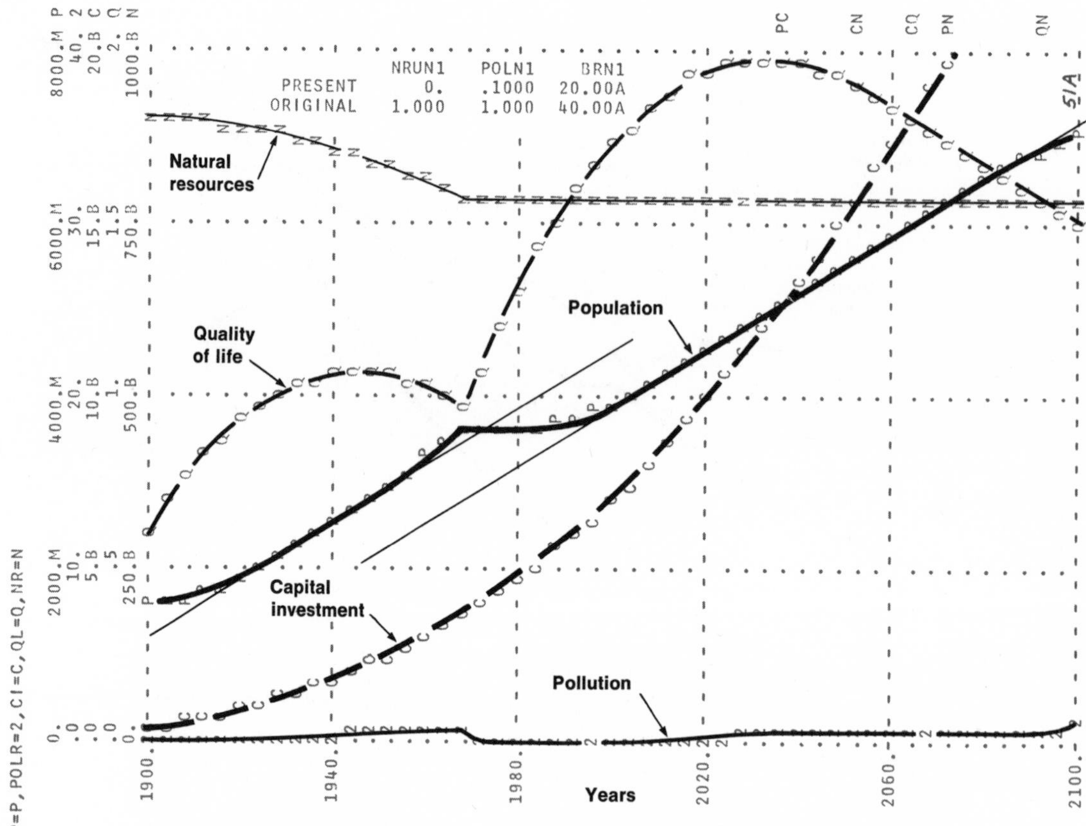

Figure 5-6 A 50% reduction in "normal" birth rate causes growth of population to pause for 20 years, then resume.

the strongest influence to start the population rising again because it increases the birth rate and decreases the death rate. The material standard of living has a compensating effect as described in Sections 3.3 and 3.11 by lowering both the birth and death rates. Comparing Figures 4-9 and 5-5, we find there is only a 30-year difference in the time at which a population of 8 billion is reached. The effect of a 30% reduction in world-wide birth rate (other things being equal) is to delay by one generation the time when 8 billion population is reached. In Figure 5-5 the capital investment rises somewhat more steeply than it did in Figure 4-9. Thus the drain on resources and the pollution problems would have been worse if these were not suppressed.

Figure 5-6 is like 5-5 except that a drastic reduction has been made in world-wide birth rate in 1970. The birth rate normal BRN1 has been reduced to half, from 0.040 to 0.020. The result is a 20-year delay in the rise of the population curve. The light lines on the figure are of the same slope and 20 years apart. Compared with Figure 4-9, the 50% reduction has delayed by 50 years the population climb to 6 billion. Figure 5-7 shows the rise in material standard of living

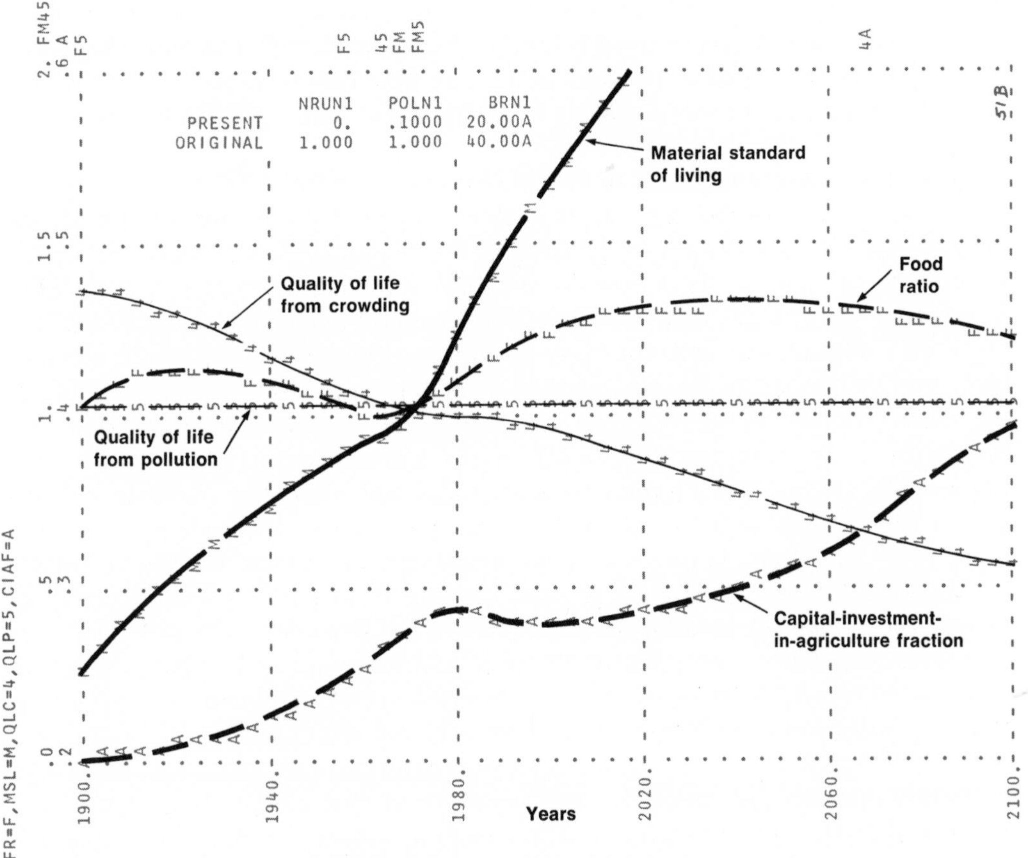

Figure 5-7 Ratios for conditions of Figure 5-6.

and the food ratio that result from the severe reduction in birth rate. Comparisons should be made between Figures 4-9, 4-10, 5-5, 5-6, and 5-7. The result seen here is typical of multiple-loop nonlinear feedback systems. An intervention applied to one of the system rates of flow is apt to have its strongest effect in some quite different variable. Here the principal consequence is in the quality of life. But the rise in quality of life might well be replaced by other changes in a more complete model and in the real-world system.

The previous computer runs have shown a strong coupling between a birth-control program and the quality of life. This occurs because, when a birth-control program is introduced, it takes the place of pressures that were previously holding down the population. In the original system the population was rising until pressures from food and other factors adjusted the rise in population to maintain balance with the remainder of the expanding socio-economic system. The reduction in birth rate normal BRN1 causes the system levels to shift their relative positions until the feedback loops in Figure 2-5 through 2-8 readjust to absorb most of the effect introduced by the change in the birth-rate coefficient BRN1.

We should note that a real-life birth-control program is of the kind introduced here. It creates an influence on the system that merely combines with the other system influences. Such a program does not establish an absolute number of births per year that are independent of shifting forces within the remainder of the system.

The larger the number of factors that enter into a particular action stream in a system, the larger are the number of feedback loops that can compensate for an intervention into the system. A detailing of the demographic section of the world system would show many influences on birth rate that are not included here. Substantial control of birth rate comes from psychological and social effects, tradition, folklore, and custom. Many of these have developed to adjust population and growth rate to be in balance with the traditions that have been accepted for quality of life. A birth-control program would actually operate within the subsystem of the demographic sector of the world system and would be surrounded by system levels representing attitudes and traditions. Many local variables within that subsystem would have an opportunity to compensate for the birth-control program before its effect would appear outside the demographic sector and have an opportunity to raise the quality of life. We would therefore expect the effect on quality of life to be much less than seen here in these computer runs. Only a detailing of the demographic sector and its local feedback loops could reveal the full extent of the probable ability of the entire system to absorb a birth-control program with little trace of effect except for a shift in certain psychological attitudes and sociological practices.

Serious doubts are raised by the behavior of this model about the effectiveness of birth control as a means of controlling population. But even if population were controlled, such control would not forestall difficulties from resource shortage and pollution, for these are more closely associated with capital investment than with population. A reduced birth rate actually raises the capital investment per person and the capability for accumulating capital.

The secondary consequences of starting a birth-control program will be to increase the influences that raise birth rate and to reduce the apparent pressures that require population control. A birth-control program which would be effective, all other things being equal, may fail because other things will not remain equal. The very incipient success of a program can set in motion forces to defeat the program.

5.3 Less Pollution

The industrialized world expects solutions for its problems to come from technology. Such has been possible in the past when technology was able to run ahead of population and exploit land and natural resources faster than population grew. But technological solutions become less possible as the ultimate world limits are approached.

In Figure 4-5 technology reduced resource usage and led to the pollution crisis. Suppose we propose now to solve the pollution crisis by another applica-

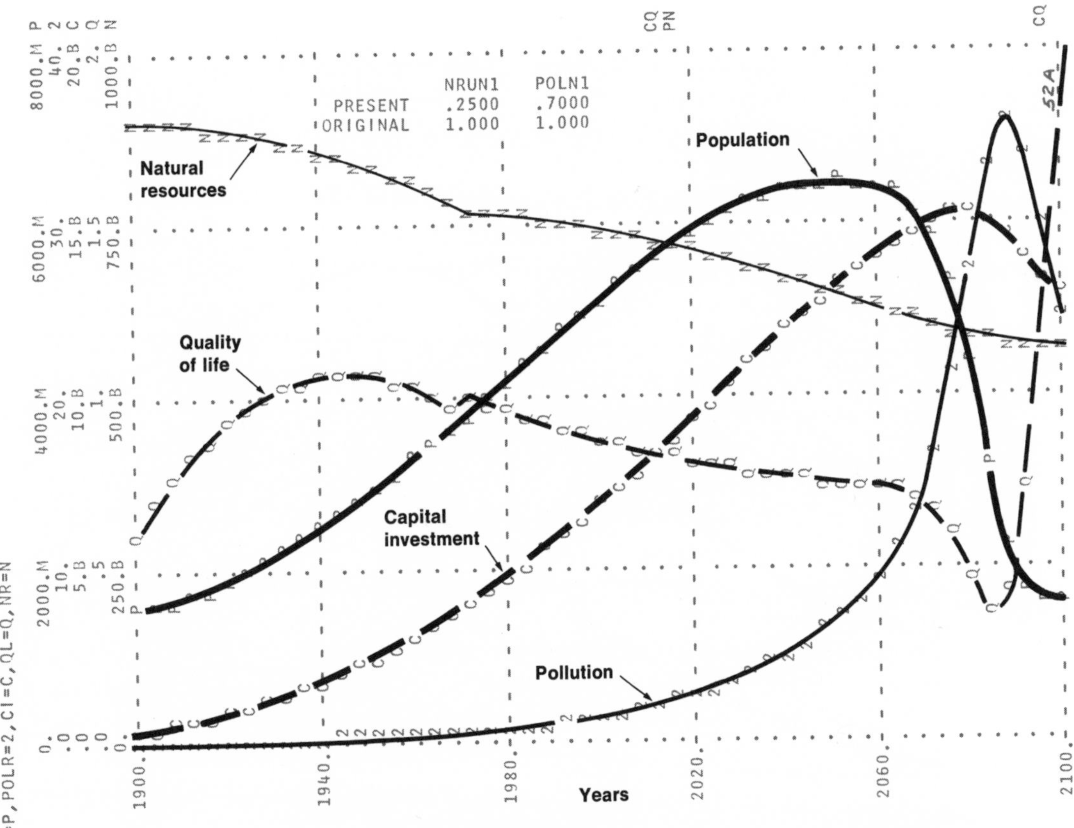

Figure 5-8 Reduction of pollution generation allows population and capital investment to increase further before the pollution crisis.

tion of technology directly to the pollution-generation processes. Figure 5-8 shows the result of reducing pollution generation, all other things being equal, by 30%. This is done by changing pollution normal POLN1 (see Section 3.31) from 1.0 to 0.7 in 1970. The result is to allow population and capital investment to grow for another 20 years before reaching a magnitude sufficient to trigger the pollution sector.

Population has risen 10% higher than in Figure 4-5 before the collapse from pollution occurs. This is typical of the effect that we can expect from major technological programs from now on. They will relieve pressures temporarily and permit population to grow to greater density before the day of reckoning comes.

The "solution" of reduced pollution has, in effect, caused more people to suffer the eventual consequences. Again, we see the dangers of partial solutions. As here, the result may be that pressures continue to build until the corrective effort is overcome. Or, the result may be to transfer the system response to another mode as can be made to happen by reducing the pollution more than in Figure 5-8. If the value of POLN1 is reduced enough (as will be seen in Figure

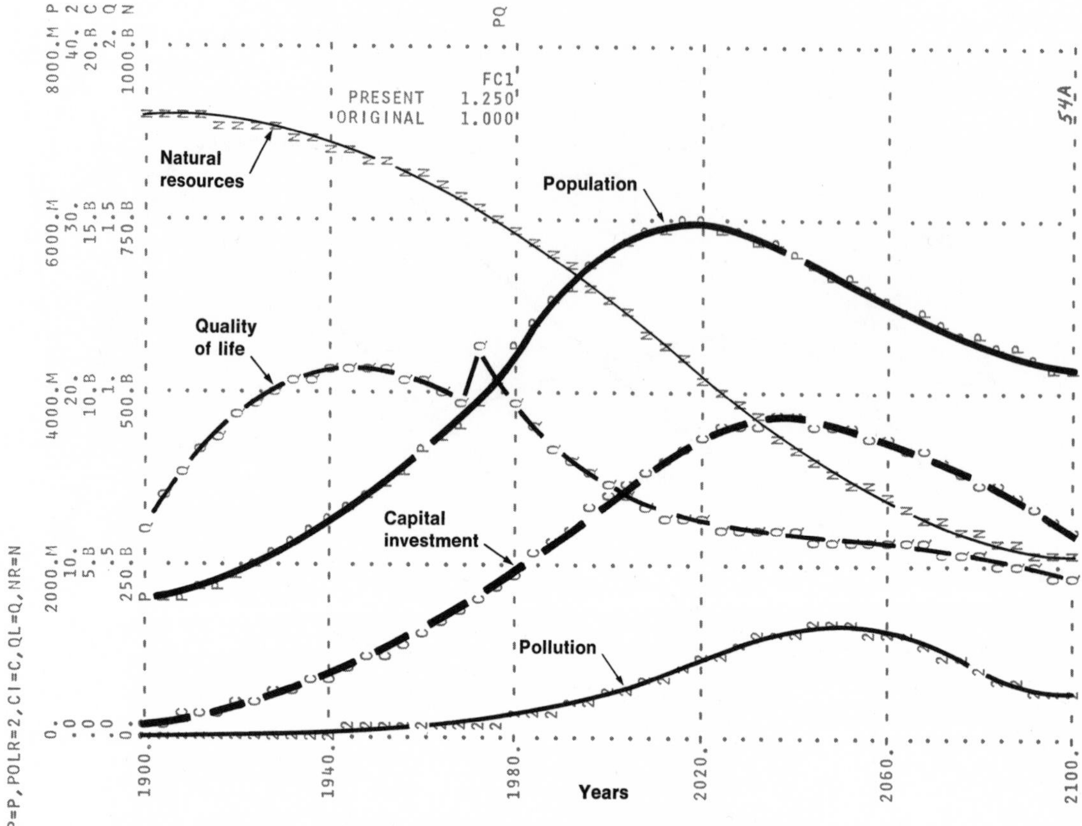

Figure 5-9 Increased food production causes increased population.

6-1), the system shifts back to the natural-resource limited mode because the pollution crisis is suppressed and demand again grows until natural resources are exhausted.

5.4 Higher Agricultural Productivity

The hope of much of the world rests on greater food production. Desert land is reclaimed. Better crop plants are developed. Irrigation dams are constructed. Forests are cleared. What is the history of such efforts over the last 2,000 years? Has the degree of undernourishment and the fraction of the population on the verge of starvation changed much? It would seem not. But how, with all the changes in population, land under cultivation, and technology could such an important system variable as the food per capita be so stable? The answer, as discussed in Chapter 2, lies in the multiple feedback loops that adjust population to exceed slightly the food supply.

The dynamics of increased food production are seen in Figures 5-9 and 5-10.

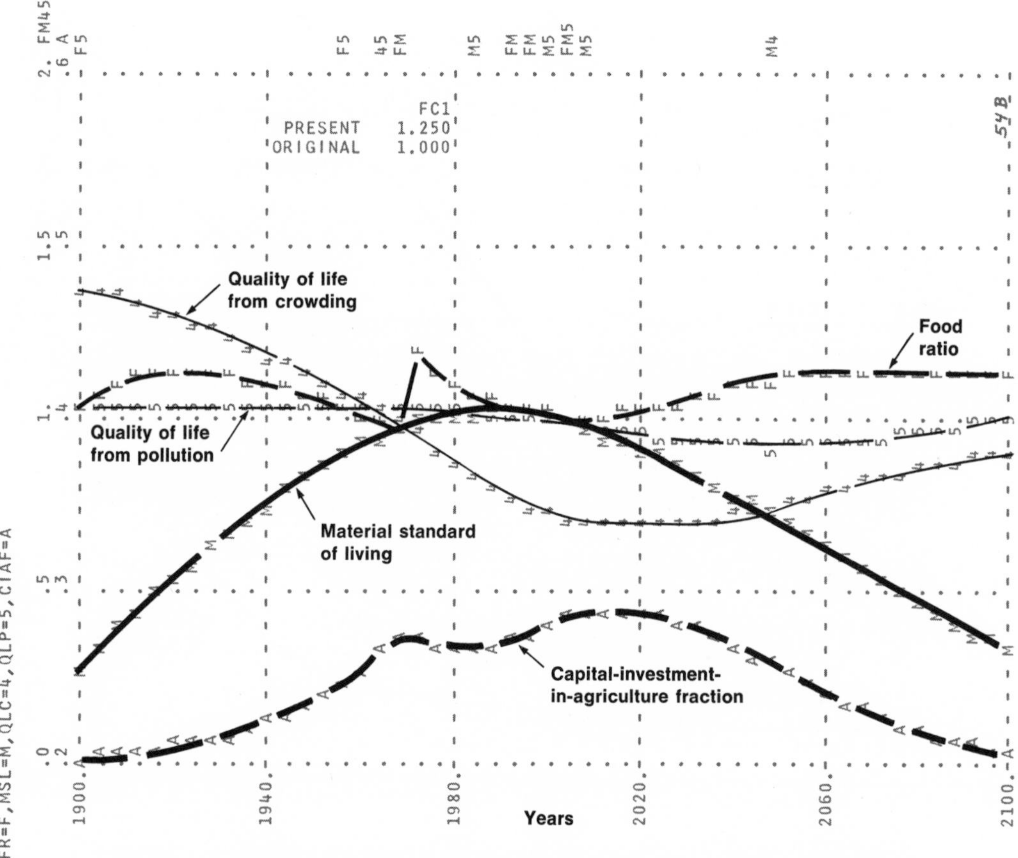

Figure 5-10 Ratios for the conditions of Figure 5-9. Higher food productivity causes capital reallocation away from agriculture.

In the year 1970 the food ratio is increased 25% by changing FC1 (see Section 3.19) from 1.0 to 1.25. This introduces an instantaneous improvement in food availability and causes the rise in quality of life seen in Figure 5-9. Compared with Figure 4-1, the effect is to increase the growth rate of population and to bring quality of life back to its original trend line in about 20 years.

A comparison of Figures 4-2 and 5-10 shows an interesting behavior in the capital-investment-in-agriculture fraction. The increased food productivity has caused a shift of capital investment out of agriculture. Certain criteria in the model give the relative desirability of food versus material standard of living just as criteria for the allocation must exist in the real world. If food productivity increases, the pressure for more food declines, and the capital allocation shifts in the direction of material goods. Even so, the material standard of living is not as high as before because of the increased population. By the year 2020 the quality of life in Figure 5-9 is slightly lower with the increased productivity of agriculture than in Figure 4-1 without.

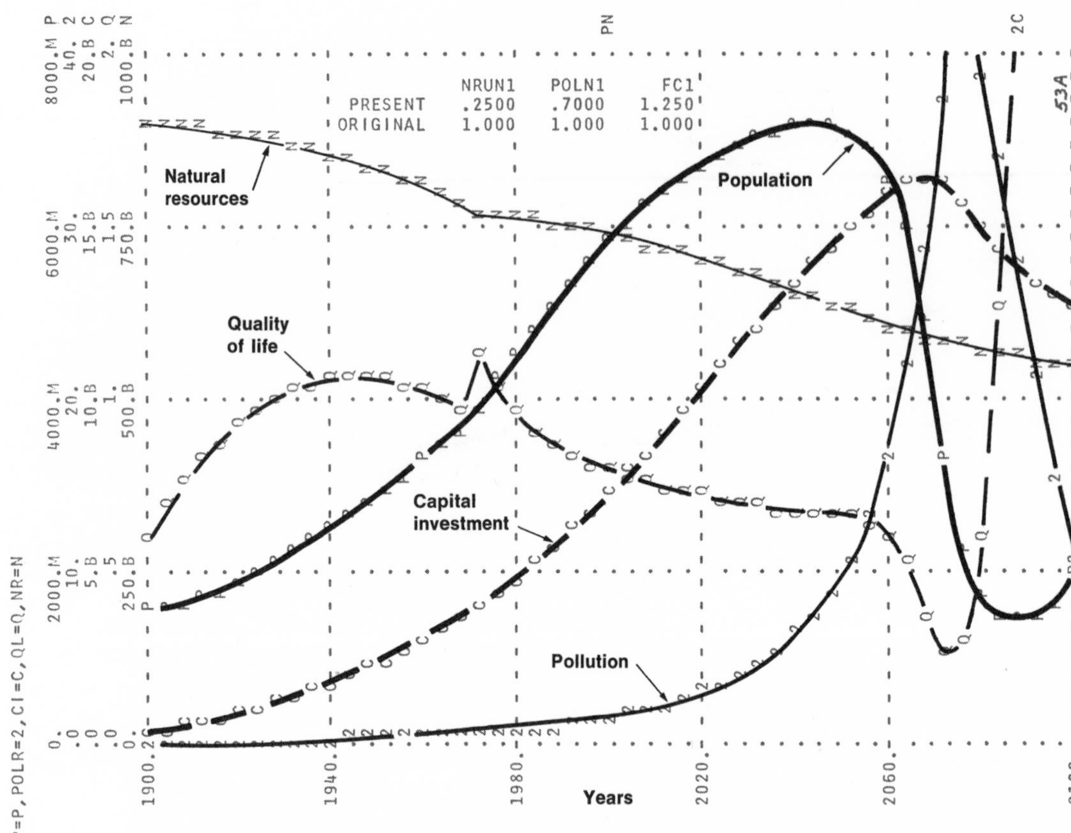

Figure 5-11 Increased food production causes greater population and earlier pollution crisis compared with Figure 5-8.

Figure 5-11 adds the same higher agricultural productivity to the conditions of Figure 5-8. The effect is to raise population higher before the pollution crisis develops. The higher availability of food allows capital to be reallocated toward material standard of living, and this permits a more rapid accumulation of capital. The higher level of capital triggers the pollution crisis about 20 years earlier than it appeared in Figure 5-8. From year 1980 onward, with the higher food productivity the quality of life is lower than before. On balance there is little change from the higher agricultural productivity, but the small changes are in an unfavorable direction.

5.5 Combination Programs

The preceding sections have examined individually the effects of increased investment rate, reduced birth rate, less pollution, and higher agricultural productivity. None are a solution to the future difficulties that face the world ecological

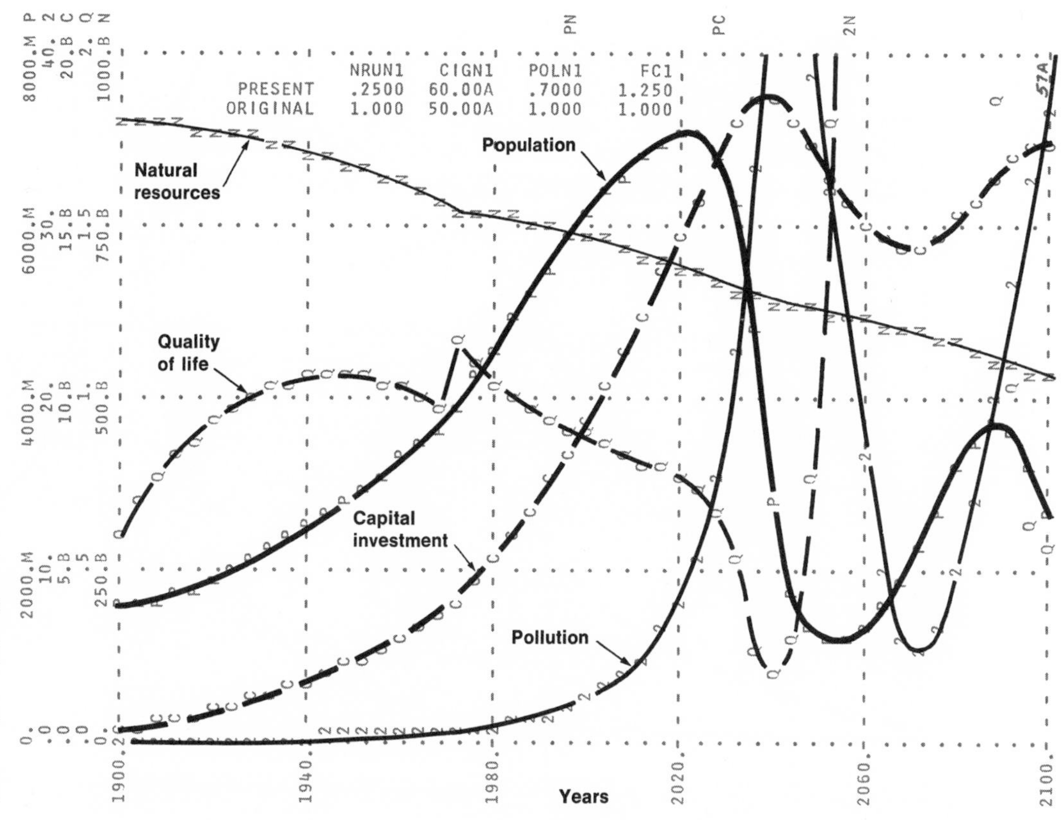

Figure 5-12 Compared with Figure 5-11, increased capital generation causes an earlier pollution crisis.

balance. The reader may feel that combinations of these programs would yield better results. We here consider such combinations.

Figure 5-11 had already combined reduced resource usage with pollution control and higher food output. To these, Figure 5-12 adds increased capital investment rate by raising CIGN1 20% in 1970. The effect is to bring on the pollution crisis 30 years sooner. Otherwise little is different.

Because Figure 5-12 encounters difficulty from pollution, more effective pollution control would normally be indicated. Figure 5-12 has already reduced POLN1 from 1.0 to 0.7. Figure 5-13 changes the pollution coefficient POLN1 to 0.4 to reduce pollution 60% from the original 1970 rate for any particular combination of population and capital investment. As was seen in Figure 5-8, the result of better pollution control is to delay the day when the fundamental causes of overtaxing the environment must be faced. Comparing Figures 5-12 and 5-13, we find that better control of pollution delays the date of population collapse by

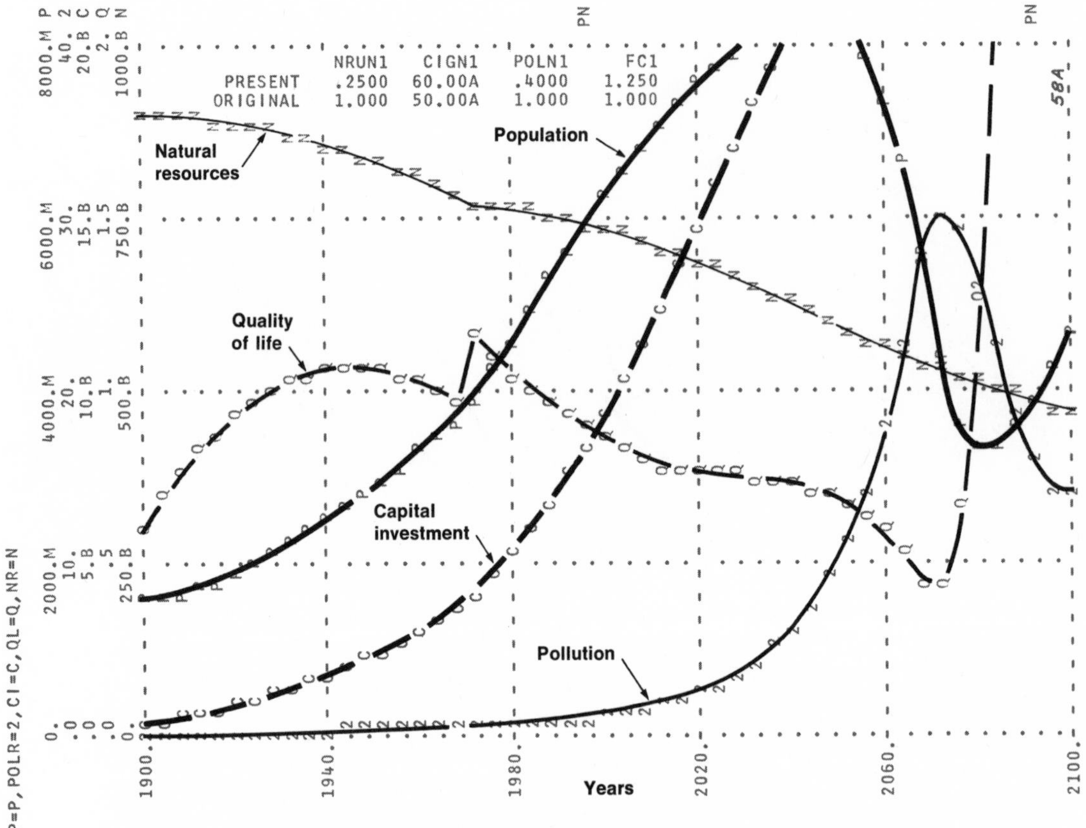

Figure 5-13 Compared with Figure 5-12, less pollution generation increases peak population and delays the pollution crisis.

20 years and allows population and capital investment to increase further before the pollution limit is reached.

In Figure 5-14 the lowered birth rate is introduced along with the conditions of Figure 5-12. BRN1 is reduced 30% in 1970. The peak of the population curve comes at the same point in time but is not as high. Capital investment has risen to about the same point and generates about the same pollution reaction.

5.6 Chapter Summary

One should not expect models of the kind discussed in this book to predict the exact form and timing of future events.* Instead, the model should be used to indicate the direction in which the behavior would alter if certain changes were made in the system structure and policies. Therefore the model runs should not be taken as predicting the year in which a condition of runaway pollution will occur.

*See Reference 2, Appendix K, on "Prediction of Time Series."

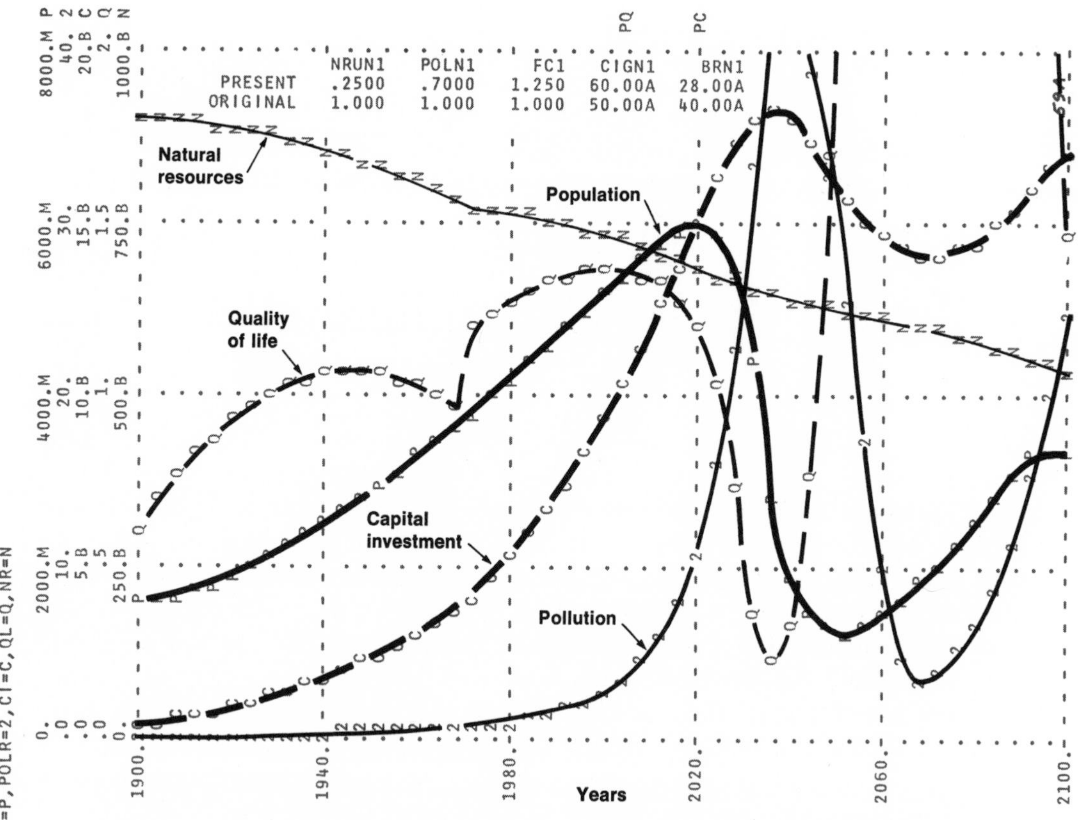

Figure 5-14 Compared with Figure 5-12, reduced birth rate lowers the peak population but does not eliminate or delay the pollution crisis.

With respect to the pollution mode of population collapse, it has already been pointed out that the geographical distributions of capital and population may differ substantially after a pollution crisis from the distributions which prevailed before. The dynamics from this model that follow the peak in population should be viewed skeptically, especially the sudden rise in quality of life that occurs in most of the computer runs. Future examination of the model will suggest modified structures that would give more likely behavior.

But the path that lies beyond the population peak is for now of minor importance. Of immediate interest are the limits to growth, the path from here to any peak that will be imposed, and the policy choices that are open. With respect to these issues, the model appears to be giving reasonable answers, even if the conclusions are contrary to present world expectations.

Within the conventional responses to economic and social problems that have been examined in this chapter, there have been no enduring solutions. If the world is to find a continuing equilibrium, it must lie in other directions.

6 Toward A Global Equilibrium

In our social systems, there are no utopias. No sustainable modes of behavior are free of pressures and stresses. But many possible modes exist, and some are more desirable than others. Usually, the more attractive kinds of behavior in our social systems seem to be possible only if we have a good understanding of the system dynamics and are willing to endure the self-discipline and pressures that must accompany the desirable mode. The world system can exhibit modes that are more hopeful than those in Chapters 4 and 5. But to develop the more promising modes will require restraint and dedication to a long-range future that man may not be capable of sustaining.

Our greatest challenge now is how to handle the transition from growth into equilibrium. The industrial societies have behind them long traditions that have encouraged and rewarded growth. The folklore and the success stories praise growth and expansion. But that is not the path of the future. Many of the present stresses in our society are from the pressures that always accompany the conversion from growth into equilibrium.

A number of studies of social systems have resulted in models that generate life cycles that start with growth and merge into equilibrium. There are always severe stresses in the transition. Pressures must rise far enough to suppress the forces that produced growth. Not only is the world facing the pressures that will stop population growth, but it also is encountering the pressures that will stop the rise of both industrialization and the world average of standard of living. The social stresses will rise still higher. The economic forces will be ones for which we have no precedent. The psychological forces will be beyond those for which we are prepared. *Urban Dynamics* shows how the pressures from shortage of land and rising unemployment accompany the usual transition from urban growth to equilibrium.* But the evidence is growing that the pressures we have seen in our cities

*Reference 5, Figure 3-1.

are minor compared to those which the world is approaching. The population pressures and the economic forces in a city that was reaching equilibrium have in the past been relieved by escape of people to new land areas. But that escape is becoming less possible. Until now we have had, in effect, an inexhaustible supply of farm land and food-growing potential. But now we are reaching the critical point where, all at the same time, population is overrunning productive land, agricultural land is almost fully employed for the first time, the rise in population is putting more demand on the food supplies, and urbanization is pushing agriculture out of the fertile areas into the marginal lands. For the first time demand is rising into a condition where supply will begin to fall while need increases. The crossover from plenty to shortage can occur abruptly.

Ahead looms the question of how growth will be stopped. Will it be by some inherent system pressure as seen in Chapters 4 and 5? Or will it be by self-imposed pressures and restraints? Many alternatives lie before us for stopping exponential growth. One choice not available is for growth to go unchecked.

All systems seem to have sensitive influence points through which the behavior of the system can be improved. As pointed out earlier, however, these influence points are usually not in the locations where most people expect them to be. Furthermore, when a sensitive influence is identified, the chances are that a person guided only by intuition and judgment will alter the control variable in the wrong direction. For example as seen in Chapter 5, although the present world emphasis is on increasing the rate of industrialization, greater industrialization is accelerating many of today's social stresses. Also, efforts are being made to increase food output even though the primary result may be to increase population and to lower the quality of life.

If growth is to be stopped, the kind of positive-feedback loops illustrated in Figures 2-2, 2-3, and 2-8 must be deactivated. Doing this through direct population control alone will almost certainly fail. Efforts to achieve population stabilization through birth-control programs probably will not prove to be effective leverage points in the system. On the other hand, capital investment and food supply are both within the major growth loops and may be points of strong influence.

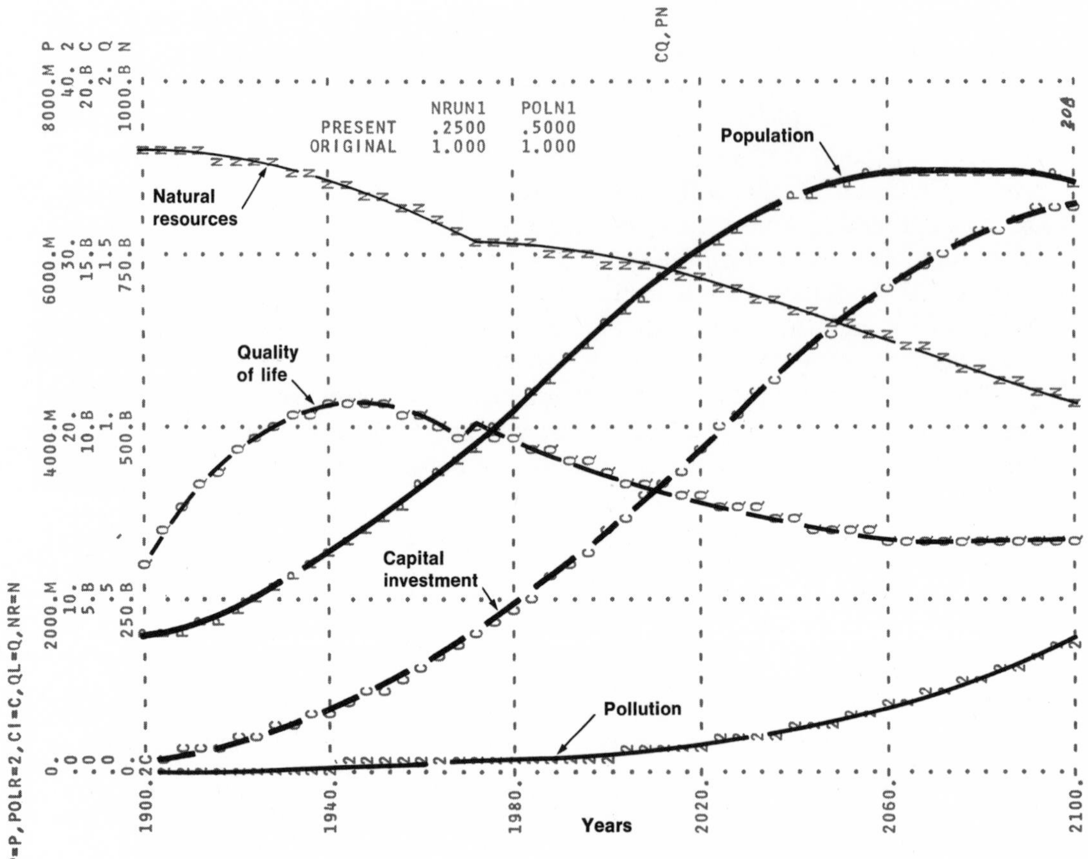

Figure 6-1 Natural-resource-usage rate and pollution generation are reduced in 1970.

Figure 6-1 is similar to Figure 5-8 except that a stricter pollution control is imposed. Here the pollution generation rate, for a given state of industrialization, is 50% of that in the original mode. Resources are used at 25% of the original rate. The pollution generation rate is just low enough to prevent the pollution crisis and to shift the system back to the resource-depletion mode. Population has peaked before the year 2100 and declines gradually in the next century (not

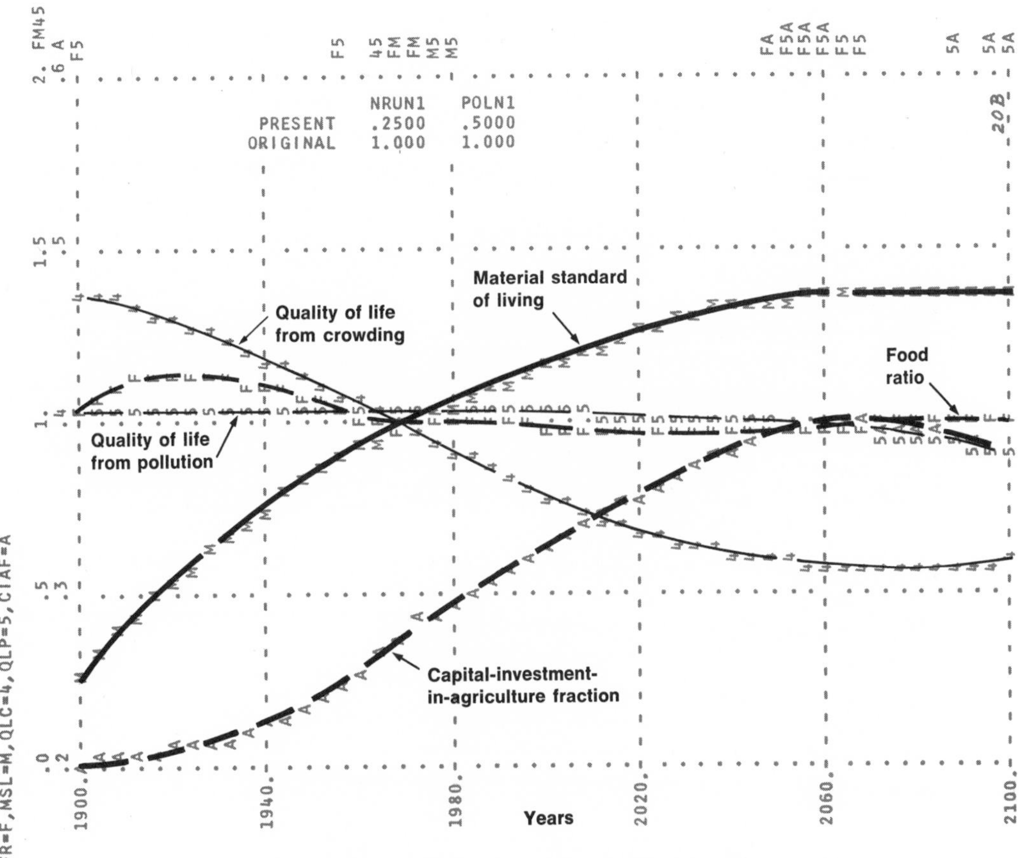

Figure 6-2 Ratios for conditions of Figure 6-1.

shown). Quality of life declines because of crowding as shown in Figure 6-2. Also, pollution has climbed until it is lowering the quality of life. If technological society is to continue, natural resources must be preserved, and with control of pollution. But efficient use of resources and substantial pollution control are not sufficient. Alone, they merely allow population and capital investment to grow until some other system limit is reached.

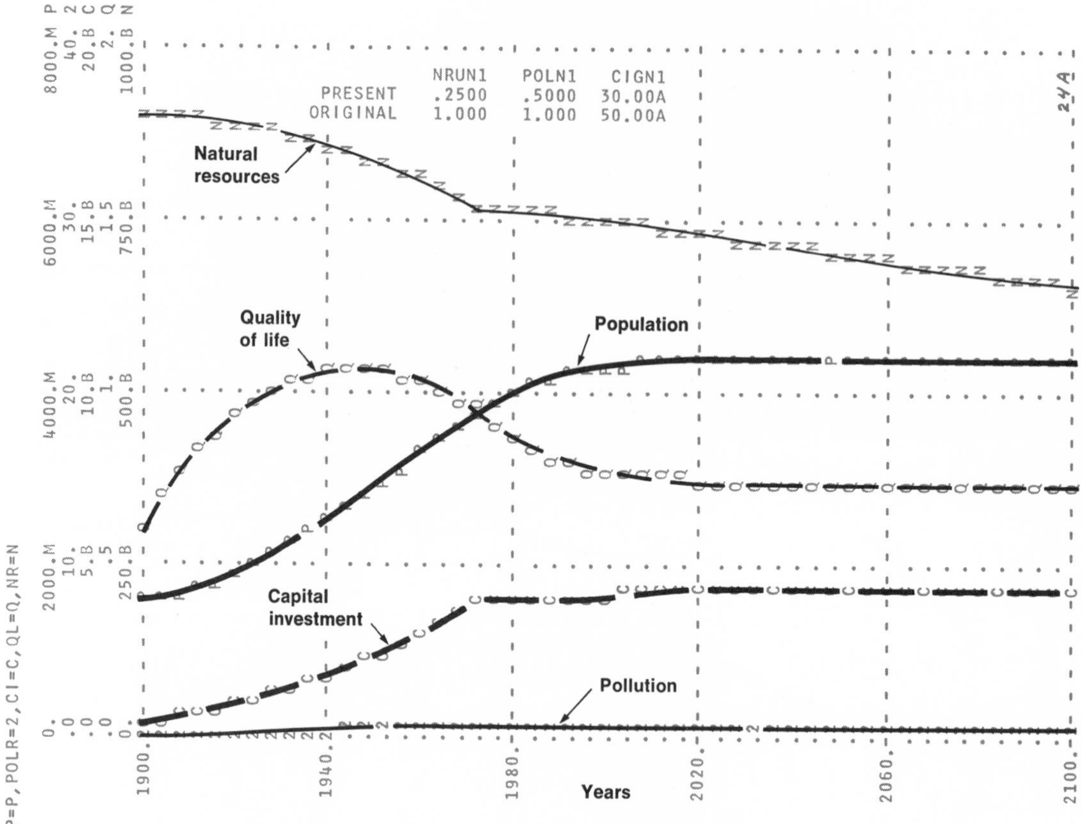

Figure 6-3 Capital generation is reduced 40% in 1970 in addition to changes in Figure 6-1. Population stabilizes at a lower level; quality of life is increased.

Figures 6-3 and 6-4 show the change resulting from a reduction of capital-investment rate in addition to the conditions of Figure 6-1. The capital-investment generation normal CIGN1 has been changed from 0.05 to 0.03 at year 1970. Population stabilizes at about 4.5 billion because the food ratio and the material standard of living have fallen far enough to establish an equilibrium with the static level of capital investment. It is important to understand that the forces for stopping growth, whatever their form, represent various kinds of pressures and influences. The total of all the pressures must rise high enough to equalize the inherent growth power within the population-industrial-food system. The necessary growth-limiting influences can come from many directions. It is probable that no single influence will be strong enough to have sufficient effect. Figures 6-3

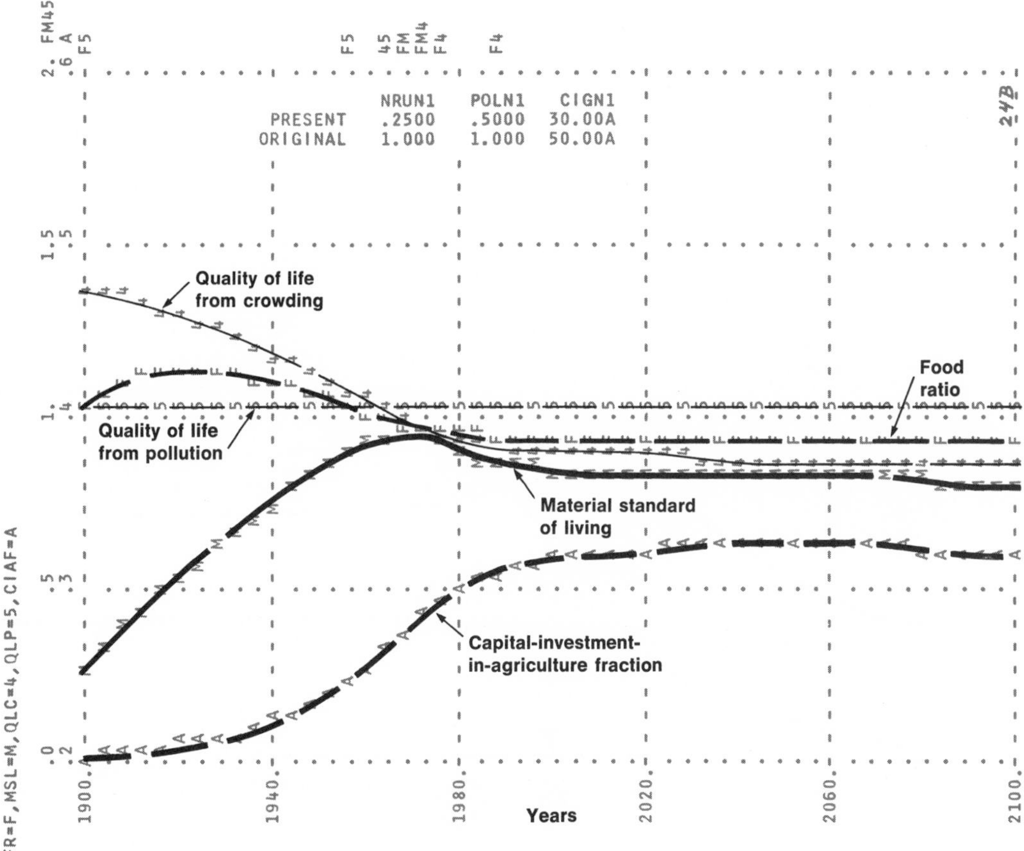

Figure 6-4 Ratios for conditions of Figure 6-3.

and 6-4 contain one change to limit growth—the reduction in the rate of capital-investment generation. The other two changes from the original model—lower natural-resource-usage rate and lower pollution generation—are changes aimed at improving the quality of life but, as such, are growth-inducing rather than growth-suppressing.

In Figure 6-3 it should be noted that the quality of life after the year 2040 is slightly higher, not lower, than in Figure 6-1 as a result of the reduced capital accumulation. In the more immediate future, quality of life in Figure 6-3 is lower as necessary if forces are to be great enough to slow the growth rate that would otherwise overtax the environment. However, in Figure 6-3 the quality of life is substantially below its peak value, and a better choice of governing policies should be sought.

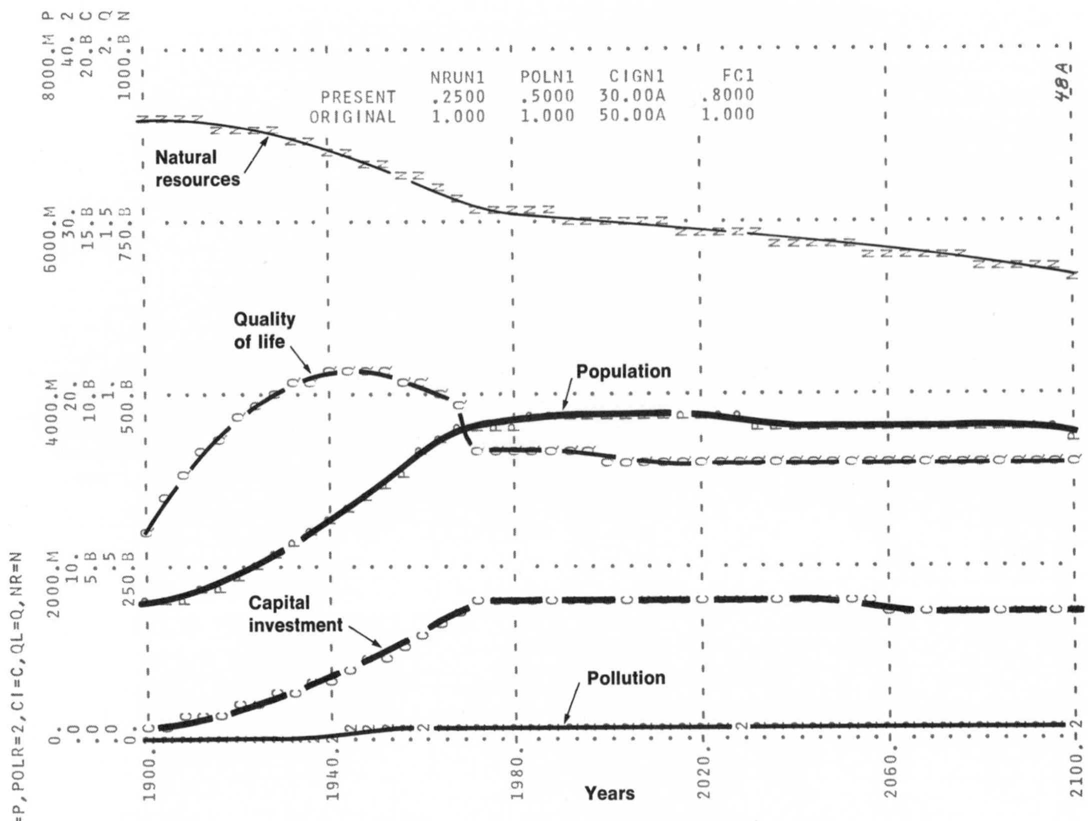

Figure 6-5 Food productivity is reduced 20% in 1970 along with changes in Figure 6-3. Population is lower, quality of life higher.

In Figures 6-5 and 6-6 the food productivity is reduced by 20% in addition to conditions of Figure 6-3. The food coefficient FC1 is reduced from 1.0 to 0.8 in 1970. The result of the 20% reduction in agricultural productivity is to reduce the actual food ratio by only 3% in equilibrium. Population has stabilized at about the 1970 level. The total quality of life has risen, as a world average, compared to Figure 6-3 and the components from material standard of living and from crowding have improved as compared to Figure 6-4. Equilibrium has been obtained, but the quality of life is still below the 1970 value.

Again it must be stressed that only pressures and influences will bring exponentially growing population and capital investment into balance with a fixed or even declining environmental capacity. The pressures can be tangible like the ones represented in Figures 6-5 and 6-6. In those figures the pressures come from lowering the emphasis on capital accumulation (including medical and health expenditures for facilities and education) and reversing the present ever-increasing emphasis on food production. Or, the pressures can come from social forces–

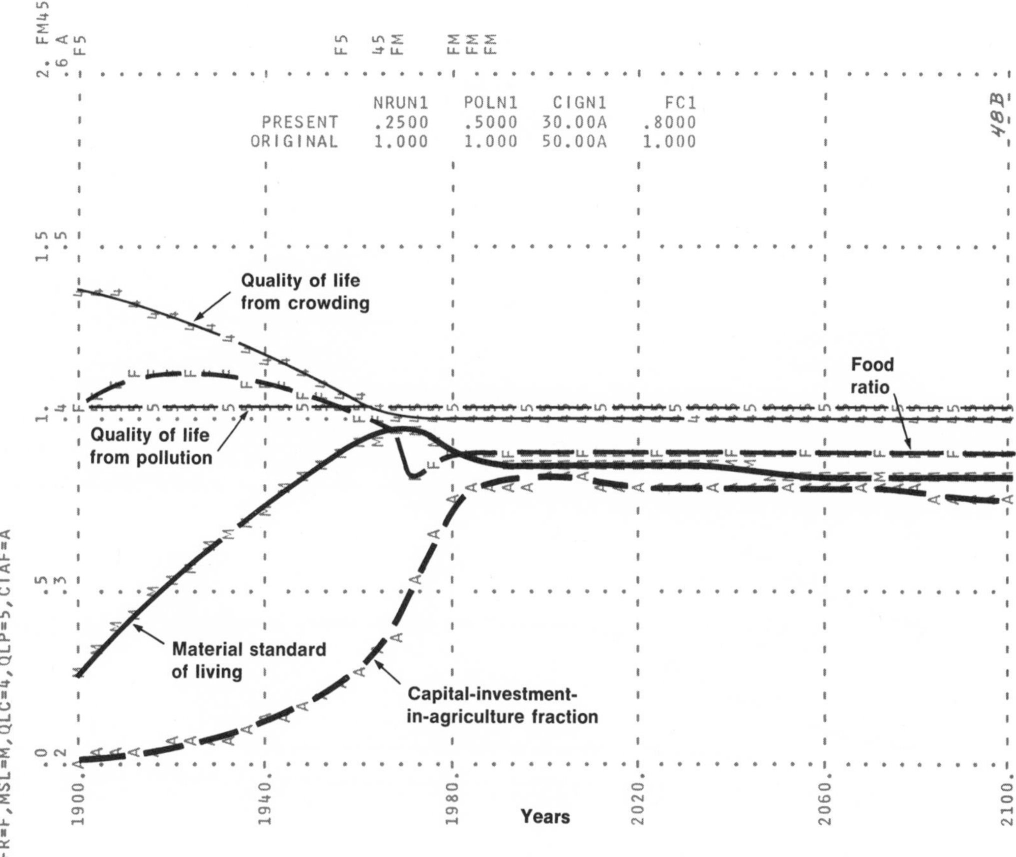

Figure 6-6 Ratios for conditions of Figure 6-5.

coercion, legal controls, reduction of personal freedom, and war. Each of the possible pressures raises major issues of humanitarianism and personal rights. The challenge is to decide the balance of pressures that will be effective and at the same time most acceptable. As a background to the deliberations on how to choose a balance of pressures, we must be always aware that the world system will make a system-determined choice for us as seen in Chapters 4 and 5 if man is unable to negotiate a more favorable compromise.

Birth control is one of the possible pressures that might be introduced to counteract the exponential growth processes that are driving population and industrialization upward. By itself, birth control does not promise sufficient effectiveness, as already discussed in Chapter 5. Alone, birth control does not lower (it probably increases) the rate of capital investment, which in turn increases pollution and depletes natural resources. But, as one influence in an ensemble of influences, population control efforts will probably be essential to ultimately raising the quality of life (subject to its not being mostly offset by changes in attitudes, values, and traditions).

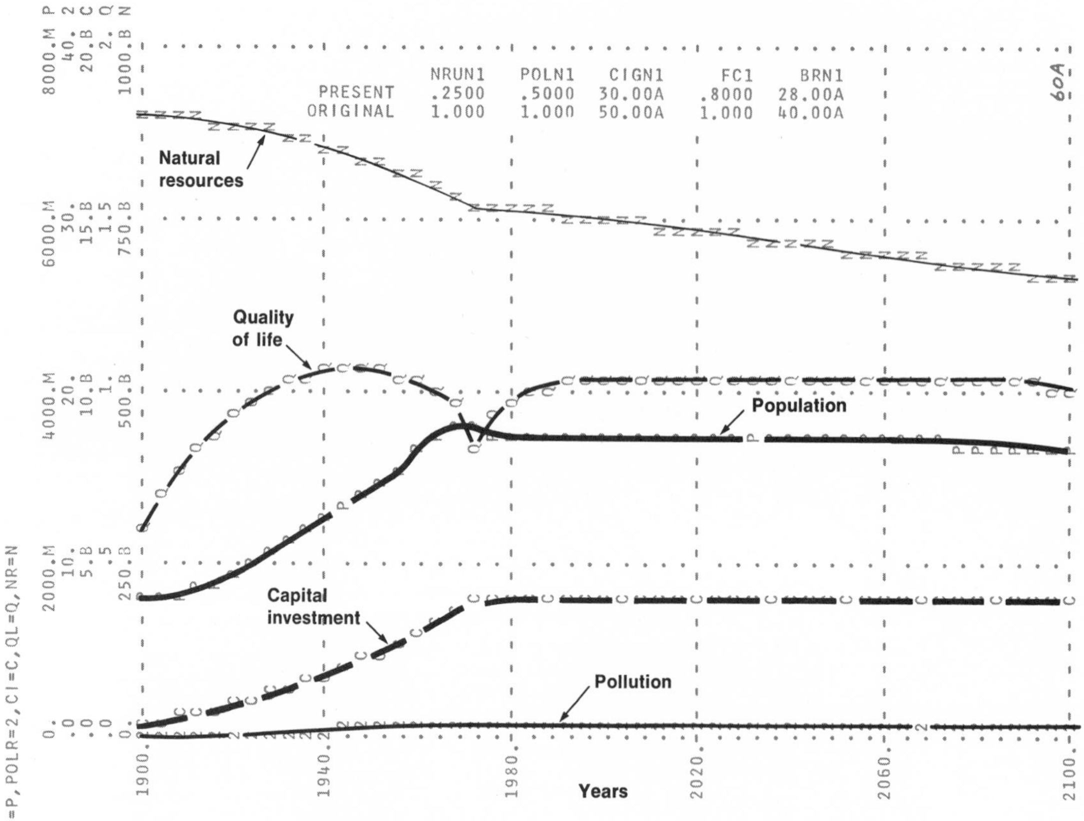

Figure 6-7 Normal birth rate reduced 30% in 1970 along with changes in Figure 6-5. Population is lower, quality of life higher again.

In Figures 6-7 and 6-8 the birth rate (other things being equal) has been reduced along with the conditions in the previous two figures. The following are the changes from the original model that are combined in this last set of figures:

Natural-resource-usage rate reduced 75%
Pollution generation reduced 50%
Capital-investment generation reduced 40%
Food production reduced 20%
Birth rate reduced 30%

The result is to drop population slightly below the 1970 value and increase the quality of life. Because of the direct influence on birth rate, the system pressures of hunger and low standard of living need not rise as high as before in order to stabilize population. Quality of life stabilizes at a value slightly higher than the 1970 value. Resources are still declining slowly and in time will depress the system unless there is sufficient recycling of waste products and substitution of

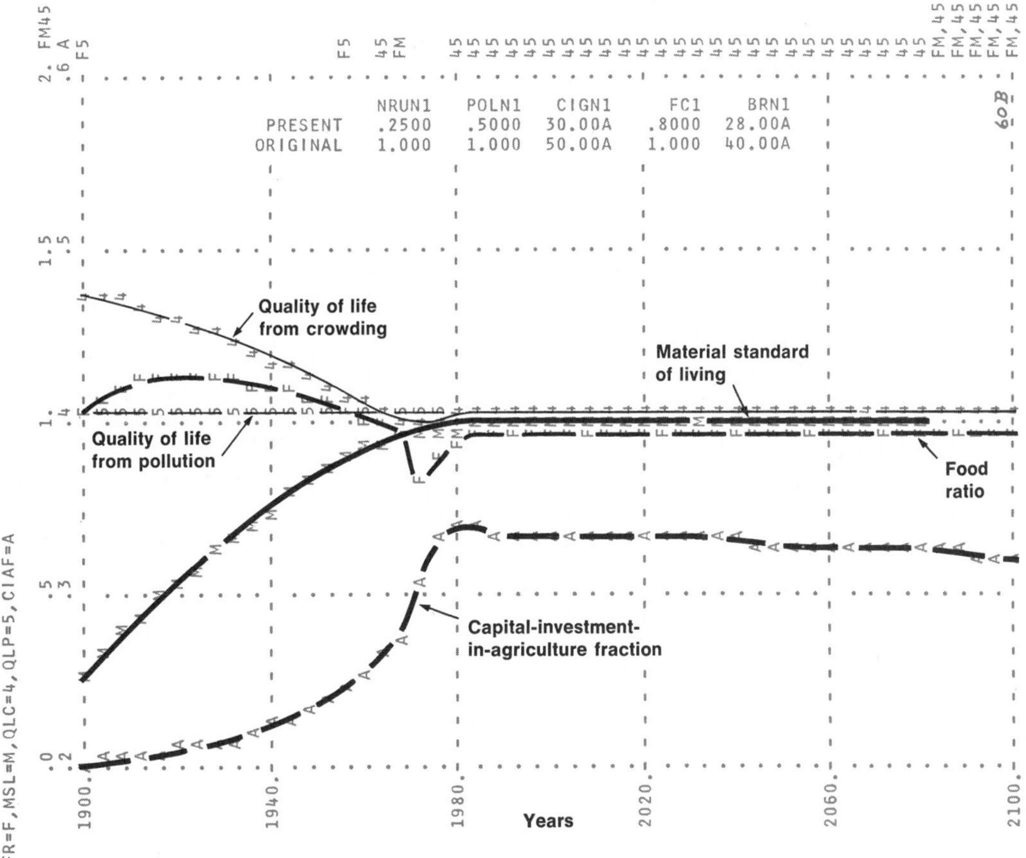

Figure 6-8 Ratios for conditions of Figure 6-7.

less critical materials.

Would the world shown by Figures 6-7 and 6-8 be accepted? It seems more attractive than the system pressures created in the earlier chapters. But is it attractive enough to gain acceptance for the changes in world social values that are implied?

Figures 6-7 and 6-8 mean an end to population growth and to rising standard of living. They suggest a reversal of the emphasis on economic development. Reduction of investment rate and reduction in agricultural productivity are counterintuitive and not likely to be accepted without extensive system studies and years of argument—perhaps more years than are available.

The reduced normal birth rate introduced in Figure 6-7 may not be achievable, particularly if the population growth rate should appear to be coming under control. Pressures on the individual and the family would not seem threatening. Each family and even each nation would feel it could expand, if others were holding steady. The result would be incentives and psychological pressures to increase birth rate and to resume population growth. As discussed in Section 5.2, a birth-control program may become merely a substitute for present psychological and social pressures that are limiting population, and, if so, the result may not be the increased quality of life that appeared in Figure 6-7. Instead, the birth-control program might cause a shift in various goals and traditions sufficient to counteract its own good effects. On the other hand, if the birth-control program becomes mandatory and is based on legal force, then the consequent loss of personal freedom is a loss in a component of quality of life that is not represented in the present model. Forcible imposition of population control would be seen by most people as a sufficiently unfavorable change in the social environment that they might prefer that the forces take the tangible forms of lowered material standard of living and reduced food supply.

This chapter suggests that a global equilibrium is conceptually possible. Whether it can be achieved is another matter. The actions that appear to be required are not apt to be accepted easily. Probably more pressure on mankind from the environment will be required before the issues will be addressed with enough concern and seriousness. But by then time to act will be even shorter.

As the next step, we can hope that the dynamics of growth and equilibrium will be investigated by more people and that the propositions presented here will be confirmed or altered until a consensus begins to form. After the consensus will still lie the task of implementing the necessary changes in world goals, values, and actions.

7 Epilogue

7.1 The Danger from Mental Models

From this book the reader should glimpse the nature of multi-loop nonlinear feedback systems, a class to which all our social systems belong. The book has shown how these systems can mislead us because our intuition and judgment have been formed to expect behavior different from that actually possessed by such systems.

The theory of world structure as described in Chapters 2 and 3 may seem oversimplified. On the other hand, the model presented here is probably more complete and explicit than the mental models now being used as a basis for world and national planning. The human mind is not adapted to interpreting the behavior of social systems. Over the long history of evolution it has not been necessary for man to understand these systems until very recent historical times. Evolutionary processes have not given us the mental skill needed to properly interpret the dynamic behavior of the systems of which we have now become a part.

This concern about the deficiencies in our mental models is not a matter to be taken lightly. The world is still pursuing programs and policies that will be at least as frustrating as those of the past. If we follow intuition, the trends of the past will continue into deepening difficulty.

7.2 The World Situation

Many global attitudes and programs seem to be based on accepting future growth in population as preordained and as the basis for action. But, if we make provision for rising population, population responds by rising. What is to stop the exponential growth? This book describes the circular processes of our social systems in which there is no uni-directional cause and effect. Instead, a ring of actions and consequences close back on themselves. One can say, incompletely, that population will grow and that cities, space, and food must be provided. But one can likewise say, also incompletely, that the provision of cities, space, and food will cause population to grow. Population generates the pressures to support growth of population. But supporting the growth leads to more population. Growth will stop only in the face of enough pressure to suppress the internal dynamic forces of expansion.

Many programs—for example the development of more productive grains and agricultural methods—are spoken of as "buying time" until population control becomes effective. But the process of buying time reduces the pressures that force population control.

Any proposed program for the future must deal with both the quality of life and the factors affecting population. "Raising the quality of life" means releasing stress, reducing crowding, reducing pollution, alleviating hunger, and treating ill health. But these pressures are exactly the sources of concern and actions that will control total population to keep it within the bounds of the fixed world within which we live. If the pressures are relaxed, so is the concern about how we impinge on the environment. Population will then rise further until the pressures reappear with an intensity that can no longer be relieved. Trying to raise quality of life without intentionally creating compensating pressures to prevent a rise in population density will be self-defeating. Efforts to improve quality of life will fail until effective means have been implemented for limiting both population and industrialization.

Without effective legal and psychological control, population grows until stresses rise far enough, which is to say that the quality of life falls far enough, to stop further increase. Everything we do to reduce those pressures causes the population to rise farther and faster and hastens the day when expediencies will no longer suffice. People are in the position of a wild animal running from its pursuers. We still have some space, natural resources, and agricultural land left. We can avoid the question of rising population as long as we can flee into this bountiful reservoir that nature provided. But the reservoir is limited. Exponential growth cannot continue. The wild animal flees until he is cornered, until he has no more space. Then he turns to fight, but he no longer has room to maneuver. He is less able to forestall disaster than if he had fought in the open while there was still room to yield and to dodge. The world is running away from its long-term threats by trying to relieve social pressures as they arise. But, if we persist in treating only the symptoms and not the causes, the result will be to increase the magnitude of the ultimate threat and reduce our capability to respond when we no longer have more space and resources to invade.

What does this mean? Instead of automatically attempting to cope with population growth, national and international efforts to relieve the pressures of excess growth must be reexamined. Many such humanitarian impulses seem to be making matters worse in the long run. Rising pressures are necessary to hasten the day when population is stabilized. Pressures can be increased by reducing food production, reducing health services, and reducing industrialization. Such reductions seem to have only slight effect on quality of life in the long run. The principal effect will be in squeezing down and stopping the runaway growth.

The limitation of capital investment may be even harder to achieve than a limit on population. There is less recognition of industrialization as a threat to the environment than there is of population. The temporarily higher standard of living that often comes from industrialization is now sought by most cultures. Damage to the environment is being caused by technological processes, but in spite of this, hope is placed instead on population control. Even if population control were achieved, rising industrialization would lead into trouble. Conversely, unless industrialization is limited directly, population control probably cannot be achieved.

7.3 Social Values

Impending changes in the world system threaten modern social values and goals. The industrialized societies have become geared to a philosophy of growth and rising standard of living for everyone. This cannot continue indefinitely. New human purposes must be defined to replace the quest for economic advancement. Nature must be helped rather than conquered. Civilization must be restrained rather than expanded. Social pressures probably must increase rather than decline, until those pressures can be transformed into a change in social values that take satisfaction from an equilibrium society.

The underdeveloped countries face equally traumatic changes in goals. They now aspire to reach the level of industrialization of the advanced countries. But they may already be in better balance with the environment than the countries they try to emulate.

Both the developed and the underdeveloped countries face the common problem of sharing the natural resources and the pollution-dissipation capacity of the earth. Without effective arbitration, only war and violence can settle the competition for a limited earth.

The long-term future of the earth must be faced soon as a guide for present action. Goals of nations and societies must be altered to become compatible with that future, otherwise man remains out of balance with his environment. Man can do vast damage first, but eventually he will yield to the mounting forces of the environment. Can the traditions of civilization be altered to become compatible with global equilibrium?

7.4 Improved Models of Social Systems

Provisionally, the answer given in this book is yes. We should be able to plot a course from exponential growth into global equilibrium.

No final recommendations have been offered here, but some pointers emerge. If we look two or three decades hence, we see that our actions today fundamentally affect that future. If we follow programs and policies chosen with knowledge of the dynamic characteristics of social systems, better alternatives can lie ahead than those to which the "natural" socio-technical-economic-political system is now leading.

We can understand more adequately the dynamic behavior of our social systems. With better insights we can expect to move toward a more attractive future.

Men would never attempt to send a space ship to the moon without first testing the equipment by constructing prototype models and by computer simulation of the anticipated space trajectories. No company would put a new kind of household appliance or electronic computer into production without first making laboratory tests. Such models and laboratory tests do not guarantee against failure, but they do identify many weaknesses which can then be corrected before they cause full-scale disasters.

Our social systems are far more complex and harder to understand than our technological systems. Why, then, do we not use the same approach of making models of social systems and conducting laboratory experiments on those models before we try new laws and government programs in real life? The answer is often stated that our knowledge of social systems is insufficient for constructing useful models. But what justification can there be for the apparent assumption that we do not know enough to construct models but believe we do know enough to directly design new social systems by passing laws and starting new social programs? I am suggesting that we do indeed know enough to make useful models of social systems. Conversely, we do not know enough to design the most effective social systems directly without first going through a model-building experimental phase. But I am confident, and substantial supporting evidence is beginning to accumulate, that the proper use of models of social systems can lead to far better systems, and to laws and programs that are far more effective than those created in the past.

The "mathematical" notation that is used for describing a dynamic model is unambiguous. It is a language that is clearer and more precise than the spoken languages such as English or French. Computer-model language is a simpler language. Its advantage is in the clarity of meaning and the simplicity of the language syntax. Once explained, the language of a computer model can be understood by almost anyone, regardless of educational background. Furthermore, any concept and relationship that can be clearly stated in ordinary language can be translated into computer-model language.

The essence of effective modeling is in the creation of a suitable model structure. How is the available information about relationships and motivations to be assembled? What structures are capable of giving the behavior modes that characterize real-life systems? What information is to be discarded as irrelevant? These questions must be answered in creating a model structure. Professional training and practice are necessary.

It is now possible to take hypotheses about the separate parts of a social system, to combine them in a computer model, and to learn the consequences. The hypotheses may at first be no more correct than the ones we are using in our intuitive thinking. But the process of computer modeling and model testing requires these hypotheses to be stated more explicitly. The model comes out of the hazy realm of mental imagery into an unambiguous representation or statement to which all have access. Assumptions can then be checked against all available information and can be rapidly improved. The great uncertainty with mental models is our inability to anticipate the consequences of interactions between the parts of a system. This uncertainty is totally eliminated in computer models.

Given a stated set of assumptions, the computer traces the resulting consequences without doubt or error. This is a powerful procedure for clarifying issues. It is not easy, however. Results will not be immediate.

7.5 The Next Frontier

We are on the threshold of a great new era in human pioneering. In the past there have been periods characterized by geographical exploration. Other periods have witnessed the formation of national governments. At other times the focus was on the creation of great literature. Most recently we have been through the pioneering frontier of science and technology. But science and technology are now a routine part of life. Science is no longer a frontier. The process of scientific discovery is orderly and organized.

I suggest that the next frontier for human endeavor will be to pioneer a better understanding of the nature of our social systems. The means are visible. The task will be no easier than the development of science and technology. For the next thirty years we can expect rapid advancement in understanding the complex dynamics of our social systems—but only with effort. Advancement will require research, the development of teaching methods and materials, and the creation of appropriate educational programs. The research results of today will, in one or two decades find their way into the secondary schools just as concepts of basic physics moved from research to general education over the past three decades.

Progress in developing a new approach to social systems will be slow. There are many crosscurrents in the social sciences that will cause confusion and delay. The proposal made here starts the modeling of social systems from the present operating arenas, uses the concepts on which our mental models are now constructed, and makes modeling a tool of the practical man who must act on the best information available to him. Political leaders, medical doctors, engineers, and managers cannot defer a decision until some future day when complete information is available. They want better understanding and guidance but are willing, if necessary, to forego perfection. This is very different from the emphasis on data gathering and statistical analysis that occupies so much of the time in social research. Data gathering has its place and is important, but it can be far more effective if it is guided by a system model that helps identify the sensitive areas of the system and points to the information that needs to be gathered.

A new professional field is emerging—the profession of social dynamics. The intensity and duration of training for a practioner in the field ought to be comparable to that in other major professions. Principles must be learned. Theory must be mastered. Cases that describe successful practice must be studied. Laboratory experiments in dynamic behavior must be performed. An internship must be served under experienced guidance.

In 1971 no such complete professional training is yet available. Parts exist. But resources in people and money are limited. As the field of social dynamics becomes more widely recognized and supported, the quality and depth of educational programs will improve. Competence of trained professionals will rise. After educational programs have been created and men have been trained, we will better understand the dynamics of our social systems. With better understanding will come better societies.

Appendices

A Equation Notation

The equations as printed in Chapter 3 and Appendix B are written in the notation for the DYNAMO compiler. For complete information see the *DYNAMO User's Manual* by Alexander L. Pugh, III, third edition, M.I.T. Press, Cambridge, Massachusetts, 1970.

The letters J, K, and L following a decimal point that separates the letters from the symbol groups representing variables are time-step indicators. The "present" time at which the equation is being evaluated is called time K. The previous point in time was J, the next is L. In rate equations, the JK notation indicates the rate that existed over the preceding time interval, and KL indicates the rate of flow that is being computed for the following time interval.

Variables and constants are designated by letter groups as defined in Appendix C.

Before the equation in Appendix B and after the equation number in Chapter 3 is a letter indicating the kind of concept that is defined by the equation. The letter L indicates a level equation, N an initial value for a level, R a rate equation, A an auxiliary variable that is part of the rate equation it feeds, C a constant, T a table, and X indicates a continuation from the preceding line.

In several equations, for example Equation 2, will be found the CLIP function. It is used here as a switch to change the value of a constant at a specified point in time. In Equation 2, the value BRN is used until TIME reaches the value specified by SWT1 after which the value is changed to that given by BRN1. The several CLIP functions are used in producing the computer runs in this book.

TABLE and TABHL are table look-up functions as for example in Equation 3. In that equation the format indicates that a table by the name of BRMMT will be entered with the variable MSL. The table extends from a value of MSL of 0 to a value of 5 in steps of 1 unit in MSL. The following line gives the required six values for the table as graphically portrayed in Figure 3-1.

B Equations of the World Model

The following equations and control information are in the exact format used by the DYNAMO compiler for producing the computer output used in this book.

```
        *       WORLD DYNAMICS W5
1       L     P.K=P.J+(DT)(BR.JK-DR.JK)
1.1     N     P=PI
1.2     C     PI=1.65E9
2       R     BR.KL=(P.K)(CLIP(BRN,BRN1,SWT1,TIME.K))(BRFM.K)(BRMM.K)(BRCM.K)(BR
        X     PM.K)
2.2     C     BRN=.04
2.3     C     BRN1=.04
2.4     C     SWT1=1970
3       A     BRMM.K=TABHL(BRMMT,MSL.K,0,5,1)
3.1     T     BRMMT=1.2/1/.85/.75/.7/.7
4       A     MSL.K=ECIR.K/(ECIRN)
4.1     C     ECIRN=1
5       A     ECIR.K=(CIR.K)(1-CIAF.K)(NREM.K)/(1-CIAFN)
6       A     NREM.K=TABLE(NREMT,NRFR.K,0,1,.25)
6.1     T     NREMT=0/.15/.5/.85/1
7       A     NRFR.K=NR.K/NRI
8       L     NR.K=NR.J+(DT)(-NRUR.JK)
8.1     N     NR=NRI
8.2     C     NRI=900E9
9       R     NRUR.KL=(P.K)(CLIP(NRUN,NRUN1,SWT2,TIME.K))(NRMM.K)
9.1     C     NRUN=1
9.2     C     NRUN1=1
9.3     C     SWT2=1970
        NOTE        EQUATION 42 CONNECTS HERE FROM EQ. 4 TO EQ. 9
10      R     DR.KL=(P.K)(CLIP(DRN,DRN1,SWT3,TIME.K))(DRMM.K)(DRPM.K)(DRFM.K)(DR
        X     CM.K)
10.2    C     DRN=.028
10.3    C     DRN1=.028
10.4    C     SWT3=1970
11      A     DRMM.K=TABHL(DRMMT,MSL.K,0,5,.5)
11.1    T     DRMMT=3/1.8/1/.8/.7/.6/.53/.5/.5/.5/.5
12      A     DRPM.K=TABLE(DRPMT,POLR.K,0,60,10)
12.1    T     DRPMT=.92/1.3/2/3.2/4.8/6.8/9.2
13      A     DRFM.K=TABHL(DRFMT,FR.K,0,2,.25)
13.1    T     DRFMT=30/3/2/1.4/1/.7/.6/.5/.5
14      A     DRCM.K=TABLE(DRCMT,CR.K,0,5,1)
14.1    T     DRCMT=.9/1/1.2/1.5/1.9/3
15      A     CR.K=(P.K)/(LA*PDN)
15.1    C     LA=135E6
15.2    C     PDN=26.5
16      A     BRCM.K=TABLE(BRCMT,CR.K,0,5,1)
16.1    T     BRCMT=1.05/1/.9/.7/.6/.55
17      A     BRFM.K=TABHL(BRFMT,FR.K,0,4,1)
17.1    T     BRFMT=0/1/1.6/1.9/2
```

```
18      A     BRPM.K=TABLE(BRPMT,POLR.K,0,60,10)
18.1    T     BRPMT=1.02/.9/.7/.4/.25/.15/.1
19      A     FR.K=(FPCI.K)(FCM.K)(FPM.K)(CLIP(FC,FC1,SWT7,TIME.K))/FN
19.1    C     FC=1
19.2    C     FC1=1
19.3    C     FN=1
19.4    C     SWT7=1970
20      A     FCM.K=TABLE(FCMT,CR.K,0,5,1)
20.1    T     FCMT=2.4/1/.6/.4/.3/.2
21      A     FPCI.K=TABHL(FPCIT,CIRA.K,0,6,1)
21.1    T     FPCIT=.5/1/1.4/1.7/1.9/2.05/2.2
22      A     CIRA.K=(CIR.K)(CIAF.K)/CIAFN
22.1    C     CIAFN=.3
23      A     CIR.K=CI.K/P.K
24      L     CI.K=CI.J+(DT)(CIG.JK-CID.JK)
24.1    N     CI=CII
24.2    C     CII=.4E9
25      R     CIG.KL=(P.K)(CIM.K)(CLIP(CIGN,CIGN1,SWT4,TIME.K))
25.1    C     CIGN=.05
25.2    C     CIGN1=.05
25.3    C     SWT4=1970
26      A     CIM.K=TABHL(CIMT,MSL.K,0,5,1)
26.1    T     CIMT=.1/1/1.8/2.4/2.8/3
27      R     CID.KL=(CI.K)(CLIP(CIDN,CIDN1,SWT5,TIME.K))
27.1    C     CIDN=.025
27.2    C     CIDN1=.025
27.3    C     SWT5=1970
28      A     FPM.K=TABLE(FPMT,POLR.K,0,60,10)
28.1    T     FPMT=1.02/.9/.65/.35/.2/.1/.05
29      A     POLR.K=POL.K/POLS
29.1    C     POLS=3.6E9
30      L     POL.K=POL.J+(DT)(POLG.JK-POLA.JK)
30.1    N     POL=POLI
30.2    C     POLI=.2E9
31      R     POLG.KL=(P.K)(CLIP(POLN,POLN1,SWT6,TIME.K))(POLCM.K)
31.1    C     POLN=1
31.2    C     POLN1=1
31.3    C     SWT6=1970
32      A     POLCM.K=TABHL(POLCMT,CIR.K,0,5,1)
32.1    T     POLCMT=.05/1/3/5.4/7.4/8
33      R     POLA.KL=POL.K/POLAT.K
34      A     POLAT.K=TABLE(POLATT,POLR.K,0,60,10)
34.1    T     POLATT=.6/2.5/5/8/11.5/15.5/20
35      L     CIAF.K=CIAF.J+(DT/CIAFT)(CFIFR.J*CIQR.J-CIAF.J)
35.1    N     CIAF=CIAFI
35.2    C     CIAFI=.2
35.3    C     CIAFT=15
36      A     CFIFR.K=TABHL(CFIFRT,FR.K,0,2,.5)
36.1    T     CFIFRT=1/.6/.3/.15/.1
37      S     QL.K=(QLS)(QLM.K)(QLC.K)(QLF.K)(QLP.K)
37.1    C     QLS=1
38      A     QLM.K=TABHL(QLMT,MSL.K,0,5,1)
38.1    T     QLMT=.2/1/1.7/2.3/2.7/2.9
39      A     QLC.K=TABLE(QLCT,CR.K,0,5,.5)
39.1    T     QLCT=2/1.3/1/.75/.55/.45/.38/.3/.25/.22/.2
40      A     QLF.K=TABHL(QLFT,FR.K,0,4,1)
40.1    T     QLFT=0/1/1.8/2.4/2.7
41      A     QLP.K=TABLE(QLPT,POLR.K,0,60,10)
41.1    T     QLPT=1.04/.85/.6/.3/.15/.05/.02
        NOTE        EQUATION 42 LOCATED BETWEEN EQ. 4 AND 9.
42      A     NRMM.K=TABHL(NRMMT,MSL.K,0,10,1)
42.1    T     NRMMT=0/1/1.8/2.4/2.9/3.3/3.6/3.8/3.9/3.95/4
        NOTE        INPUT FROM EQN. 38 AND 40 TO EQN. 35
43      A     CIQR.K=TABHL(CIQRT,QLM.K/QLF.K,0,2,.5)
43.1    T     CIQRT=.7/.8/1/1.5/2
        NOTE
        NOTE  CONTROL CARDS
        NOTE
43.5    C     DT=.2
43.6    C     LENGTH=2100
43.7    N     TIME=1900
44      A     PRTPER.K=CLIP(PRTP1,PRTP2,PRSWT,TIME.K)
44.1    C     PRTP1=0
```

```
44.2    C       PRTP2=0
44.3    C       PRSWT=0
45      A       PLTPER.K=CLIP(PLTP1,PLTP2,PLSWT,TIME.K)
45.1    C       PLTP1=4
45.2    C       PLTP2=4
45.3    C       PLSWT=0
        PLOT    P=P(0,8E9)/POLR=2(0,40)/CI=C(0,20E9)/QL=Q(0,2)/NR=N(0,1000E9)
        PLOT    FR=F,MSL=M,QLC=4,QLP=5(0,2)/CIAF=A(.2,.6)
        RUN     ORIG
```

C Definitions of Terms

Following are the definitions of the letter groups used to identify variables and constants in the model equations.

BR	BIRTH RATE (PEOPLE/YEAR)
BRCM	BIRTH-RATE-FROM-CROWDING MULTIPLIER (DIMENSIONLESS)
BRCMT	BIRTH-RATE-FROM-CROWDING-MULTIPLIER TABLE
BRFM	BIRTH-RATE-FROM-FOOD MULTIPLIER (DIMENSIONLESS)
BRFMT	BIRTH-RATE-FROM-FOOD-MULTIPLIER TABLE
BRMM	BIRTH-RATE-FROM-MATERIAL MULTIPLIER (DIMENSIONLESS)
BRMMT	BIRTH-RATE-FROM-MATERIAL-MULTIPLIER TABLE
BRN	BIRTH RATE NORMAL (FRACTION/YEAR)
BRN1	BIRTH RATE NORMAL NO. 1 (FRACTION/YEAR)
BRPM	BIRTH-RATE-FROM-POLLUTION MULTIPLIER (DIMENSIONLESS)
BRPMT	BIRTH-RATE-FROM-POLLUTION-MULTIPLIER TABLE
CFIFR	CAPITAL FRACTION INDICATED BY FOOD RATIO (DIMENSIONLESS)
CFIFRT	CAPITAL-FRACTION-INDICATED-BY-FOOD-RATIO TABLE
CI	CAPITAL INVESTMENT (CAPITAL UNITS)
CIAF	CAPITAL-INVESTMENT-IN-AGRICULTURE FRACTION (DIMENSIONLESS)
CIAFI	CAPITAL-INVESTMENT-IN-AGRICULTURE FRACTION, INITIAL (DIMENSIONLESS)
CIAFN	CAPITAL-INVESTMENT-IN-AGRICULTURE FRACTION NORMAL (DIMENSIONLESS)
CIAFT	CAPITAL-INVESTMENT-IN-AGRICULTURE-FRACTION ADJUSTMENT TIME (YEARS)
CID	CAPITAL-INVESTMENT DISCARD (CAPITAL UNITS/YEAR)
CIDN	CAPITAL-INVESTMENT DISCARD NORMAL (FRACTION/YEAR)
CIDN1	CAPITAL-INVESTMENT DISCARD NORMAL NO. 1 (FRACTION/YEAR)
CIG	CAPITAL-INVESTMENT GENERATION (CAPITAL UNITS/YEAR)
CIGN	CAPITAL-INVESTMENT GENERATION NORMAL (CAPITAL UNITS/PERSON/YEAR)
CIGN1	CAPITAL-INVESTMENT GENERATION NORMAL NO. 1 (CAPITAL UNITS/PERSON/YEAR)
CII	CAPITAL INVESTMENT, INITIAL (CAPITAL UNITS)
CIM	CAPITAL-INVESTMENT MULTIPLIER (DIMENSIONLESS)
CIMT	CAPITAL-INVESTMENT-MULTIPLIER TABLE
CIQR	CAPITAL-INVESTMENT-FROM-QUALITY RATIO (DIMENSIONLESS)
CIQRT	CAPITAL-INVESTMENT-FROM-QUALITY-RATIO TABLE
CIR	CAPITAL-INVESTMENT RATIO (CAPITAL UNITS/PERSON)
CIRA	CAPITAL-INVESTMENT RATIO IN AGRICULTURE (CAPITAL UNITS/PERSON)
CLIP	LOGICAL FUNCTION USED AS A TIME SWITCH TO CHANGE PARAMETER VALUE
CR	CROWDING RATIO (DIMENSIONLESS)
DR	DEATH RATE (PEOPLE/YEAR)
DRCM	DEATH-RATE-FROM-CROWDING MULTIPLIER (DIMENSIONLESS)
DRCMT	DEATH-RATE-FROM-CROWDING-MULTIPLIER TABLE
DRFM	DEATH-RATE-FROM-FOOD MULTIPLIER (DIMENSIONLESS)
DRFMT	DEATH-RATE-FROM-FOOD-MULTIPLIER TABLE

DRMM	DEATH-RATE-FROM-MATERIAL MULTIPLIER (DIMENSIONLESS)
DRMMT	DEATH-RATE-FROM-MATERIAL-MULTIPLIER TABLE
DRN	DEATH RATE NORMAL (FRACTION/YEAR)
DRN1	DEATH RATE NORMAL NO. 1 (FRACTION/YEAR)
DRPM	DEATH-RATE-FROM-POLLUTION MULTIPLIER (DIMENSIONLESS)
DRPMT	DEATH-RATE-FROM-POLLUTION-MULTIPLIER TABLE
ECIR	EFFECTIVE-CAPITAL-INVESTMENT RATIO (CAPITAL UNITS/PERSON)
ECIRN	EFFECTIVE-CAPITAL-INVESTMENT RATIO NORMAL (CAPITAL UNITS/PERSON)
FC	FOOD COEFFICIENT (DIMENSIONLESS)
FC1	FOOD COEFFICIENT NO. 1 (DIMENSIONLESS)
FCM	FOOD-FROM-CROWDING MULTIPLIER (DIMENSIONLESS)
FCMT	FOOD-FROM-CROWDING-MULTIPLIER TABLE
FN	FOOD NORMAL (FOOD UNITS/PERSON/YEAR)
FPCI	FOOD POTENTIAL FROM CAPITAL INVESTMENT (FOOD UNITS/PERSON/YEAR)
FPCIT	FOOD-POTENTIAL-FROM-CAPITAL-INVESTMENT TABLE
FPM	FOOD-FROM-POLLUTION MULTIPLIER (DIMENSIONLESS)
FPMT	FOOD-FROM-POLLUTION-MULTIPLIER TABLE
FR	FOOD RATIO (DIMENSIONLESS)
LA	LAND AREA (SQUARE KILOMETERS)
MSL	MATERIAL STANDARD OF LIVING (DIMENSIONLESS)
NR	NATURAL RESOURCES (NATURAL RESOURCE UNITS)
NREM	NATURAL-RESOURCE-EXTRACTION MULTIPLIER (DIMENSIONLESS)
NREMT	NATURAL-RESOURCE-EXTRACTION-MULTIPLIER TABLE
NRFR	NATURAL-RESOURCE FRACTION REMAINING (DIMENSIONLESS)
NRI	NATURAL RESOURCES, INITIAL (NATURAL-RESOURCE UNITS)
NRMM	NATURAL-RESOURCE-FROM-MATERIAL MULTIPLIER (DIMENSIONLESS)
NRMMT	NATURAL-RESOURCE-FROM-MATERIAL-MULTIPLIER TABLE
NRUN	NATURAL-RESOURCE USAGE NORMAL (NATURAL RESOURCE UNITS/PERSON/YEAR)
NRUN1	NATURAL-RESOURCE USAGE NORMAL NO. 1 (NATURAL RESOURCE UNITS/PERSON/YEAR)
NRUR	NATURAL-RESOURCE-USAGE RATE (NATURAL RESOURCE UNITS/YEAR)
P	POPULATION (PEOPLE)
PDN	POPULATION DENSITY NORMAL (PEOPLE/SQUARE KILOMETER)
PI	POPULATION, INITIAL (PEOPLE)
PLSWT	PLOT SWITCH TIME (YEARS)
PLTP1	PLOT PERIOD NO. 1 (YEARS)
PLTP2	PLOT PERIOD NO. 2 (YEARS)
PLTPER	PLOT PERIOD (YEARS)
POL	POLLUTION (POLLUTION UNITS)
POLA	POLLUTION ABSORPTION (POLLUTION UNITS/YEAR)
POLAT	POLLUTION-ABSORPTION TIME (YEARS)
POLATT	POLLUTION-ABSORPTION-TIME TABLE
POLCM	POLLUTION-FROM-CAPITAL MULTIPLIER (DIMENSIONLESS)
POLCMT	POLLUTION-FROM-CAPITAL-MULTIPLIER TABLE
POLG	POLLUTION GENERATION (POLLUTION UNITS/YEAR)
POLI	POLLUTION, INITIAL (POLLUTION UNITS)
POLN	POLLUTION NORMAL (POLLUTION UNITS/PERSON/YEAR)
POLN1	POLLUTION NORMAL NO. 1 (POLLUTION UNITS/PERSON/YEAR)
POLR	POLLUTION RATIO (DIMENSIONLESS)
POLS	POLLUTION STANDARD (POLLUTION UNITS)
PRSWT	PRINT SWITCH TIME (YEARS)
PRTP1	PRINT PERIOD NO. 1 (YEARS)
PRTP2	PRINT PERIOD NO. 2 (YEARS)
PRTPER	PRINT PERIOD (YEARS)
QL	QUALITY OF LIFE (SATISFACTION UNITS)
QLC	QUALITY OF LIFE FROM CROWDING (DIMENSIONLESS)
QLCT	QUALITY-OF-LIFE-FROM-CROWDING TABLE
QLF	QUALITY OF LIFE FROM FOOD (DIMENSIONLESS)
QLFT	QUALITY-OF-LIFE-FROM-FOOD TABLE
QLM	QUALITY OF LIFE FROM MATERIAL (DIMENSIONLESS)
QLMT	QUALITY-OF-LIFE-FROM-MATERIAL TABLE
QLP	QUALITY OF LIFE FROM POLLUTION (DIMENSIONLESS)
QLPT	QUALITY-OF-LIFE-FROM-POLLUTION TABLE
QLS	QUALITY-OF-LIFE STANDARD (SATISFACTION UNITS)
SWT1	SWITCH TIME NO. 1 FOR BRN (YEARS)
SWT2	SWITCH TIME NO. 2 FOR NRUN (YEARS)
SWT3	SWITCH TIME NO. 3 FOR DRN (YEARS)
SWT4	SWITCH TIME NO. 4 FOR CIGN (YEARS)
SWT5	SWITCH TIME NO. 5 FOR CIDN (YEARS)
SWT6	SWITCH TIME NO. 6 FOR POLN (YEARS)

SWT7	SWITCH TIME NO. 7 FOR FC (YEARS)
TABHL	LOGICAL FUNCTION, TABLE LOOK UP AND INTERPOLATION
TABLE	LOGICAL FUNCTION, TABLE LOOK UP AND INTERPOLATION
TIME	CALENDAR TIME (YEARS)

References

1. Banfield, Edward C. *The Unheavenly City*. Little, Brown and Company, Boston, 1970.
2. Forrester, Jay W. *Industrial Dynamics.* The M.I.T. Press, Cambridge, Massachusetts, 1961.
3. Forrester, Jay W. *Principles of Systems.* (Preliminary Edition, ten chapters) Wright-Allen Press, Room 516, 238 Main Street, Cambridge, Massachusetts 02142, 1968.
4. Forrester, Jay W. "Market Growth as Influenced by Capital Investment," *Industrial Management Review*, Vol. IX, No. 2, Winter 1968, pp. 83-105.
5. Forrester, Jay W. *Urban Dynamics.* The M.I.T. Press, Cambridge, Massachusetts, 1969.
6. Foster, Richard O. "The Dynamics of Blood Sugar Regulation." M.Sc. Thesis, Department of Electrical Engineering, Massachusetts Institute of Technology, Cambridge, July 1970.
7. Meadows, Dennis L. *Dynamics of Commodity Production Cycles.* Wright-Allen Press, 238 Main Street, Cambridge, Massachusetts 02142, 1970.
8. Peccei, Aurelio. *The Chasm Ahead.* The Macmillan Company, London, 1969.
9. Peccei, Aurelio. "Where Are We? Where Are We Going?," *Successo,* Vol. XII, No. 1 New Series pp. 119-126 (February 1970), published by Aldo Palazzi, Editore, Via Suretti 34, Milan, Italy.
10. Peccei, Aurelio. "The Predicament of Mankind," *Successo,* Vol. XII No. 6 New Series pp. 149-156 (June 1970), published by Aldo Palazzi, Editore, Via Zuretti 34, Milan, Italy.
11. Roberts, Edward B. *The Dynamics of Research and Development.* Harper & Row, New York, 1964.

Index